MW00436108

THE PANCAKE MAN & FRIENDS

For Katherine & Narsh —
I hope you enjoy this!

All my best,
Richard Speight
10/16/92

RICHARD SPEIGHT

THE PANCAKE MAN & FRIENDS

STORIES THAT RAISE THE SPIRIT AND WARM THE HEART

DIMENSIONS
FOR LIVING

NASHVILLE

THE PANCAKE MAN AND FRIENDS

Copyright © 1992 by Richard Speight

All rights reserved.
No part of this work may be reproduced or transmitted in any form or by any means, electronic or mechanical, including photocopying and recording, or by any information storage or retrieval system, except as may be expressly permitted by the 1976 Copyright Act or in writing from the publisher. Requests for permission should be addressed in writing to Dimensions for Living, 201 Eighth Avenue South, Nashville, TN 37203.

This book is printed on recycled, acid-free paper.

Library of Congress Cataloging-in-Publication Data

Speight, Richard.
    The pancake man and friends: stories that raise the spirit and warm the heart/Richard Speight.
       p. cm.
    ISBN 0-687-30006-1 (alk. paper)
    I. Title.
PS3569.P442P3   1992
813'.54—dc20   91-46432
                                                   CIP

MANUFACTURED IN THE UNITED STATES OF AMERICA

*This book is lovingly dedicated to
Barbara, Barby, Lindy, and Richard, Jr.,
and to all of the men and women who ever
climbed the stairs to the Challenge Class.*

Their encouragement made this book happen.

ACKNOWLEDGMENTS

I am grateful to Barbara, Barby, Lindy, and Richard, Jr. for letting me write about them and loving me anyway.

I am grateful to Barbara for affirming and encouraging me, for her excellent editing of my work, and for her valuable contributions during the rewriting process.

I am grateful to Dr. John Griscom for setting high standards and challenging me to meet them.

I am grateful to Dr. John Killinger for believing a book was possible and for pushing me in the right direction.

I am grateful for all of the people who were a part of my life whose stories made it to these pages. Each of them has blessed me in a special way.

Most of all, I am grateful to God, who sent His spirit to me day after day, bringing joy into my heart and breathing life into my words. The glory is His.

CONTENTS

THE PANCAKE MAN

I have no idea when the tradition started.

Who knows why some things become "traditions" within families, while other things occur once and are forgotten? It just happens, I suppose. All I know is that by the time my oldest daughter, Barby, was no more than five or six years old, the tradition of the Pancake Man was already firmly entrenched. She's grown and married now, which means that this little bit of family lore has been around for a long, long time.

There was a day, however, when I thought for sure that the Pancake Man had died, and that's what this is about. It isn't about how the tradition started. It's about how it almost ended.

Let me begin by setting the record straight. I am, in fact, the Pancake Man. The one and only. Accept no substitutes.

Before Barbara and I started having children, I had a vision of what I wanted fatherhood to be like. I wanted to be a "pal" to my children and more besides. I aspired to be a dispenser of wisdom, a benevolent guide who would lead his children along the mine-infested pathway to maturity, gently nudging them this way and that, helping them make the journey safely. It was a big job; it would take a big man to do it. I never once envisioned myself in a role as mundane as that of the Pancake Man.

Why did the Pancake Man catch on? Why did he become a legend in his own time?

Maybe it was because I appeared so out of place in the kitchen, even in that role. My being in there for any purpose, even something as innocuous as making pancakes, must have seemed like a big deal to our little ones. Perhaps it was because I attacked the task with such obvious enthusiasm from the very first. I couldn't just go in there and make pancakes. Oh, no! I had to assume a second identity, step out of my unimaginative self and enter upon the task with a flourish. I had to make it fun, exciting, and extraordinary. I couldn't just do it.

My enthusiasm was a carryover from my childhood. As far back as I can remember, I have loved pancakes, especially buckwheats. I would stack them up, cover them with butter, watch the butter trickle down the side of the stack as it melted, then soak them in syrup from a metal can, the one that looked like a real log cabin. I would cut the stack into wedge-shaped sections and stick my fork through the whole wedge, so that each delicious bite consisted of layer after layer of still-warm pancake, laced with butter and soaked in syrup.

It was more than a meal. It was an experience. I almost salivate when I think about it. Even now I can't drive past an I-Hop without getting an urge to sit down to a stack of buckwheats. It was altogether natural, then, that I would want the same kind of memorable experience for my children. Thus it is no surprise that the legend of the Pancake Man was born. I made it fun, because for me, it was fun.

Early on, the Pancake Man became a regular Saturday morning visitor at our house. I would take my place in front of the stove at the drop of a suggestion. The cast iron griddle of my youth had turned to Teflon and the little metal log cabin had become a plastic squeeze bottle, but the same great smell still filled the house, and the same sense of satisfaction still accompanied the completion of the meal. I derived great pleasure from knowing that the good feelings from my childhood were being appropriately preserved and passed along to the next generation.

The simple thing, of course, would have been to just make pancakes and skip the silly stuff. Why have an alter ego? Why assume a separate identity? And how did that title, the Pancake Man, come about, anyway?

It sort of evolved, actually.

As in many families, our children were usually up first on Saturday morning. Often as not, they would come racing into our bedroom and pile onto the bed, ready for some fun.

One Saturday morning, one of them brought up the subject of pancakes. Instead of doing so in the usual way, however, he or she, I don't recall which, asked in complete innocence if the Pancake Man could come that morning. I grabbed the ball and ran with it. I told them that I'd heard that the Pancake Man was in town, and that if they would wait in the breakfast room, who knows what might happen? Once they had scrambled off, I slipped into the kitchen, donned an apron and a chef's hat, grabbed a spatula, and burst through the door to the breakfast room. Voila! The Pancake Man was born!

After that, the routine was set in concrete. At some point on Saturday morning, one of the three would ask that all-important question. "Daddy? Do you think the Pancake Man will come this morning?" That would set the other two off. "Yeah, Daddy! Do you think there's a chance? Can you get him to come? Try, Daddy! Please!"

"I hear he's in the neighborhood," I'd reply once more, eager to play my role.

Was there ever a time when he couldn't come? Are you kidding? My heart would melt faster than a dollop of butter on a hot buckwheat whenever they started in with the game. Forget about sleeping late! Forget about a quiet cup of coffee and a relaxed session with the paper! Of course he'd come! Bolstered by their infectious enthusiasm, I'd mentally assume my "other" identity, arm myself with spatula and ladle, and head off in search of the pancake mix. No sooner would the first round of cakes be bubbling on the griddle than our stair-step trio of tykes would come marching in, ready to chow down.

For a while, there was an official outfit. On that first morning, I had conscripted the red-checkered apron and chef's hat Barbara had bought for me to use in my role as Outdoor Grill Man. That ensemble quickly became part of the game, but after a while it no longer mattered what I was wearing. From time to time I would inject variety by making pancakes of different sizes or by making them in the shape of the children's initials, but by and large, it was just regular pancakes and a room full of happy people.

Sometimes I would be asked to play the role of the Waffle Man. This is a somewhat more sophisticated version of the standard Pancake Man tradition and one that carries with it considerably more risk. Remember, I'm a professional. You shouldn't try this at home.

It's pretty hard to mess up a pancake. I've flipped a few clean off of the griddle in my time, but for the most part, pancake errors are few and far between and are seldom noticed by the ones waiting to eat. If you mess up a pancake, you can make another in a hurry and cover your mistake. But when you are standing in front of a lone waffle iron, the pressure is on.

Think about it. Three little faces turned toward me like so many open-beaked birds in a nest, depending on me to fill their needs. Three hands holding on to junior forks. Three sets of eyes watching my every move; three button noses soaking up the delicious aroma steaming from the cooking waffle. Then comes the moment they've been waiting for.

I jiggle the handle cautiously, then confidently pull upward. The waffle splits in the middle, each half permanently stuck to its respective side of the waffle iron. I smile lamely. Disappointment fills the room. Depression becomes my companion.

Believe me, it has happened more than once. It takes a while to recover from a trauma as big as that!

The Waffle Man is high-risk business. The Pancake Man managed to survive, however, and through the years, pancakes evolved into a kind of comfort food for our family. The Pancake Man became an important part of our existence.

Time passed, as it always does. Days became weeks, weeks yielded to months, and months mystically blended to form years. Before we knew it, our three stairsteps had grown up and were beginning to wander off in different directions. Barbara and I clung to the past, wishing with all our hearts that we could stick our fingers in the hourglass and stop the painful, inexorable passage of time.

Then came the fateful day.

It was the Saturday after New Year's, not too long ago. That's when it happened. I had been up for a while. Everyone else was still in bed. I was sipping coffee in the quiet of our breakfast room. All of a sudden the idea hit me. Why not surprise the children? It's a tradition! And it's been such a long time. They'll love it! Really they will.

I stepped into my imaginary phone booth, ripped off my everyday image, exposed the bright-red "P" on my chest, and emerged as the Pancake Man!

What a great idea, I thought, as I scurried about, making preparations. Barby, our oldest, would be moving back to her dorm at Vanderbilt the next day. Lindy, the second in the line, would be flying back to Davidson College at the same time. "Bet they don't have anything this good at school," I mused as I plopped the Teflon griddle on the computer-regulated, heat-sensitive burner, and turned the switch to 450 degrees. Richard, the youngest, was still a year away from college, but I knew he'd appreciate this surprise every bit as much as his sisters. I decided to let

Barbara sleep late. This would be daddy's special time with the children.

Visions of Ozzie and Harriet filled my head as the familiar sweet smell wafted through the house. I eagerly anticipated the coming experience. The four of us would gather around the table, hum "Getting to Know You" in three-part harmony, then sink our teeth into a delicious stack of pancakes. What a warm, wonderful family moment it would be.

A few minutes later, I began knocking on bedroom doors.

I started at Barby's room. There was no response. I knocked again. Still no response. I eased the door open and stuck my head in. The place was dark as a tomb.

"The Pancake Man is here," I chirped. Her answer was a low, gutteral moan. "Come on to the kitchen when you're ready," I added cheerily, easing back out and closing the door.

Lindy's room was next. Again, no response to my knock. When I cracked the door, a shaft of light fell across her bed. "Lindy," I sang out. "The Pancake Man is here!" I thought I detected the slightest upward movement in one of her eyelids, but it slammed shut so quickly it was hard to tell.

"Lindy, the Pancake Man is here," I said less cheerily.

You should have seen it. One hand came out from under her covers, followed by the other. They moved slowly upward toward her pillow. Then in one smoothly executed, world-class maneuver, she simultaneously flopped from her back to her stomach and flipped the pillow over to cover her head.

"Come on when you're ready," I said. My voice had all the confidence of a principal inviting a student to drop by the office for a little discipline.

I wasn't daunted. It was a temporary setback, that's all. After all, weren't our children known to be legendary sleepers? They actually die for a while; their bodies become one with the bed—a single unit dedicated to a single purpose.

I headed for Richard's room. His head was already under his pillow. There must be some kind of underground warning system at work, I thought.

"Rise and shine," I called out. "The Pancake Man's in town. He'll be along any minute."

"What time is it?" Richard groaned.

"Almost ten," I responded, my enthusiasm waning.

"You're kidding!" he cried out, his tousled mop of unruly hair pointing in every conceivable direction. "What're you doing up so early? It's Saturday, for Pete's sake!"

I headed back to the kitchen, turned the temperature under the griddle to simmer, put some plastic wrap over the batter bowl, and returned to my morning newspaper.

Finally, they began to wander in.

Richard came first. His eyelids drooped and his jaw sagged. He didn't even turn on the Saturday morning cartoons. He just sat there, teetering on the brink of unconsciousness.

Lindy came next. She forced out some cheerful words, but I could tell that her heart wasn't in it.

Barby finally appeared. The other two seemed downright peppy compared to her. She had sent her body as her official representative, but had left her mind and her spirit in the sack.

The three of them sat in stony silence while I stacked up the cakes and placed them in front of their semicomatose bodies. They ate in silence as I scurried about. The only sound was the clinking of forks and the gulping of milk.

One by one they got up from the table.

Richard said nothing. He just walked over to me, patted me gently on the back, then returned to his room.

Lindy carried her plate to the counter. "Thank you, Daddy," she said, one eye still firmly closed.

Barby gave me a hug. "I love you, Daddy," she said. I

thought she was going to fall asleep on my shoulder, but she managed to regain consciousness and headed back to bed.

The kitchen was deathly quiet. I started to clean up. That's when I noticed it. Lindy and Richard had only picked at their food. Fully half of their pancakes remained, a soggy reminder of their noble effort. Barby's plate was clean, but moments later I found her pancakes sitting dolefully in the sink, still stacked, untouched. They looked as sad as I felt.

Everything changes, I thought. Nothing remains the same. The Pancake Man has outlived his usefulness. He has died a natural death. It's time to let him rest in peace.

Winter came and went, and I thought no more about it. The children were in and out, sometimes at odd intervals, and not always at the same time. I purposely avoided all recollections of that experience. I didn't want to remind myself of the melancholy feeling that had come with it.

In April, Lindy came home for her spring break, ready to rest and recuperate. She had a good week, resting a lot, visiting friends, and sharing a few laughs with us old folks, too. On her last Saturday morning I cooked pancakes again. I left out all the fanfare, though. Enough is enough. Don't make a big deal out of it, I reminded myself.

We had a nice conversation while she ate. Then I wandered off to do something else. When I came back a while later, Lindy had finished and had cleared the table. There was one plate still on the table, however. It was at the place where I sit.

In the middle of that plate, sitting on a napkin, was a single cold pancake. On that pancake, Lindy had drawn a happy face with a red magic marker. It wasn't an ordinary happy face. It had glasses, a pointed nose, and a forelock that hung down over its forehead. It looked suspiciously like me!

On the napkin, she had written these words:
Thanks, Pancake Man!

The tradition wasn't dead, it was just different.

What are family traditions, anyway? Tangible evidence of loving memories, that's what. They're all of those funny, silly, sometimes ridiculous things that remind us of how much we love each other, how much fun we've had, and how nice it is when love is in full bloom. Traditions don't die. Traditions are love, and love doesn't die. Love evolves, but it doesn't die.

I stared at that silly pancake. Tears started to flow. I felt very blessed. I quickly said a prayer of thanksgiving, then carried the treasured happy face off to show it to Barbara.

Now that's the kind of love that makes life worthwhile.

God's love abides forever. That's the good news for eternity. Human love is made in the image of God's love, just as surely as we are made in the image of God. Human love abides, too. It really can make life worth living. That's the good news, the wonderful news, for the here and now.

HIS NAME WAS JOHN

I can't remember when I first met John. It wasn't all that important at the time. As with many of life's events, there was no advance notice of its eventual significance.

I called him "Big John" from the first. He wasn't big in the physical sense, but I definitely perceived him that way. He was a "whole" person, full of energy, in love with life. That kind of person always seems big to me.

He and I were the same height, but he looked taller because of his lankiness, which was exaggerated by the gangly lope of his walk. He moved as though his joints didn't exist, as if the bones in his arms and legs were held in close proximity only by skin. When he walked, his arms and legs seemed to be going in several directions at once. When he stood still, his legs bowed outward at the knees and came back together at the feet like huge parentheses. His thick, black hair was matched by a bushy, black monobrow; both contrasted sharply with his pale complexion. A smile lit up his face, giving the world just the smallest hint of the devilishness behind it.

John was a "good ol' boy." There's no other way to say it. He wasn't a redneck, just a good ol' boy in the best sense of that phrase. The pot-bellied image of the stereotypical Southerner didn't fit John. He was pleasant, happy-go-lucky, omnipresent, and ever faithful. He was a nice guy.

The four of us, Judy and John, Barbara and Richard, first became friends at church. We soon became inseparable. Ours was an unlikely alliance, to say the least. John was country raised, had little formal education, and, as far as I knew, didn't own a necktie, except for the out-of-style knit antique that hung uneasily around his neck every Sunday. I was his antithesis, a button-down guy who had just completed a monumental struggle with law school and the bar exam, a forerunner of the modern-day yuppie. For me relaxing meant unbuttoning my vest.

John was content in his job with a local loan company and seldom talked in terms of success, at least not as I would have identified it. I was ambitious and determined to climb to the top of the heap. Yet in spite of our differences, we hit it off from the start.

Looking back, I can see why I was attracted to him. There was a simplicity, an honesty, and a non-competitiveness about him that contrasted sharply with so many of my success-motivated associates. He was a welcome refuge.

Our respective tasks often took us to a common location—the Davidson County Courthouse. Many's the time I have spotted that familiar disjointed lope from a distance, feeling the comfort of recognition emotionally before my mind had time to confirm his identity. I'd hurry to catch up, then the two of us would take a break together and share the day's joys and tribulations. I always felt better for the experience.

One of John's chief characteristics was his incredible willingness to lend a hand. It was almost dangerous for me to mention any pending project or problem in his presence. He would invariably show up at my house with the proper tools and the proper attitude, committed to the successful completion of the task. It didn't matter how difficult or challenging the project, or how serious I was in suggesting it. John was ready.

Sometimes his willing spirit got us in over our heads. The concrete patio is a good example.

"I really don't think we ought to do this," I said, trying to hide the fear in my voice. We were standing in the middle of my backyard at the time. "I don't know anything about concrete," I lamented.

"Shucks, Ree-chard," he drawled in his soft southern voice, mispronouncing my name as usual. "I watched some guys do it once. It's simple! Besides, we're a whole lot smarter than they were. If they can do it, so can we."

John was forever deciding that he and I were probably more intelligent than the people we would have to pay to do various things, therefore we ought to be able to do them ourselves and save a little money.

"We'll figure it out," he added confidently.

With that declaration, he picked up his hoe and began chopping away at the precious turf that I had fertilized and mowed for several years and had grown to love.

Confidence was his long suit. Who was I to discourage him?

Another of his philosophies was that the best way to make yourself "do" the impossible was to "undo" what you had. That way, you'd have no choice but to finish. Want a new sink? Take the old one out. Want to repaint? Strip off the old finish. Want a concrete patio? You get the picture.

A few hours later there we were, standing in the middle of a huge bare spot next to my back door, dripping sweat, dreaming about a patio. Then the huge truck arrived.

We soon discovered that when it comes to working with concrete, how smart you are is not the issue. We also discovered that once the mixer starts sending that heavy gray glop down the chute, there's no turning back.

The mixer operator just laughed at first. Finally he recognized the seriousness of our plight. If he hadn't come to our rescue, we'd still be standing there, knee-deep in

hardened concrete, sheepishly trying to explain what
went wrong.

We barely survived. I'd never been so completely spent
in my life, and John looked every bit as bad as I felt.
Lacking the strength to stagger indoors, we just lay there
in the grass, each having lost much of his body weight and
all of his will to live. Finally, John struggled to his knees,
picked up a stick, crawled to the patio and scratched "JWR
+ RDS" in the jelling concrete.

"If I don't wake up tomorrow, I at least want Judy to
know what it was that killed me," he moaned.

I was always a little embarrassed by those initials. It
looked like "JWR loves RDS." Now that I think about it,
though, I guess that was true.

While "the great patio caper" might have been the most
difficult, it was only one of many tasks we undertook
together. We'd try anything. What we lacked in money,
we made up for in nerve. We painted everything that
didn't move, installed a huge television antenna that
dwarfed us both, refinished countless pieces of furniture,
did all kinds of amateur carpentry and plumbing, and
generally kept things in pretty good shape. There was no
end to John's willingness to help, and no end to Judy's
willingness to let him spend his time helping me and
others.

John's real value as a friend, however, had little to do
with these acts of kindness. He was as dependable
emotionally as he was physically. I could say what I felt in
his presence, without fear of judgment, rejection, or
criticism. John never put me down and he never betrayed
my confidence.

What a gift it is to have the patience and sensitivity to
listen to, and really hear, another human being. John made
me feel that I was okay, no matter how silly my idea or
how dirty my laundry. When I felt low, when things
weren't going my way, or when I had news to share, good
or bad, I'd call Big John. Years passed. Our friendship

deepened. Our storehouse of treasured memories over-flowed.

One year, in mid-October, John began to talk about changing jobs. That may have been routine for some people, but not for John. Loyalty was ingrained in his soul, and his job was his security. Security was more important than money or anything else. Security was success. He longed for it. He liked feeling that he was where he belonged, that he was wanted. He needed that feeling. Though he wasn't being paid a great deal, the man he worked for treated him with kindness and affection. We both thought the business might someday be his. Leaving would be difficult. Expenses were rising, though. Baby Jonathan had come, and even though the future looked promising, John began to realize that a little more money right now would be nice, too.

John struggled with this weighty problem throughout November and on into December. Then one day he just made up his mind and gave notice. He would start his new job on the first of January. None of us was certain that he had done the right thing, not even John. But once it was decided, it was decided.

He and I talked a lot that Christmas. Barbara and Judy talked, too. Young Richard, our third child, had arrived only a few months after Jonathan. Judy had no family in Nashville, and she leaned on Barbara, drawing from her experience.

Judy was worried about the coming change in jobs, and she freely admitted it. She was worried about John's life-style at home, too. Where he had once been a bundle of energy, constantly puttering about the house and finding things to do, now he was tired all the time. When he came home for the evening he was finished for the day. And there was that cough, that nagging, constant cough we all had noticed. John didn't smoke, and there was no reason for him to be coughing so much. He had sought help, but none of his doctors knew what caused it, much less what to do about it. The four of us tried to be cheerful when we were together, but it was becoming more and more difficult.

To make matters worse, right around that time a new interstate highway came through and took all of John and Judy's backyard. The fence was to come within five feet of the corner of their house. The neighbor on one side lost only a small part of his lot, while the other neighbor's property was taken completely. John's house was in the worst possible spot.

It seemed so unfair! All of his trees would be gone, as would his workshop, which was his pride and joy. He had spent countless hours out there, tinkering with broken appliances, refinishing old furniture and making things for his friends. The government couldn't have hurt him more if it had taken everything! He was devastated.

The new year came and went and the new job started. John was no longer downtown, so I saw him much less often. I missed him terribly. An important part of my daily routine was suddenly gone, and it hurt. There was a big void in my life.

In March of that year, Barbara gave a surprise party to celebrate my thirtieth birthday. Who came early to help decorate? Big John, of course. Barbara memorialized the event with home movies. John was right in the thick of things, looking a bit haggard, but very proud of the part he had played in the surprise.

The next week, John went to the hospital for routine tests. His doctors continued to be stumped by his nagging cough. Judy insisted that it was no big deal. He'd be in and out in a matter of a day or so, she assured us. We believed her.

Barbara and I were on our way somewhere else a few days later when we both felt the urge to drop by the hospital. We acted on that urge, thank God. We never got wherever we were supposed to be going.

Moments before we arrived, the doctor had broken the

bad news to our dear friends. When we got to his hospital room, John was on the phone, trying his best to sound casual, trying to convince his parents that cancer was no big thing.

What do you say at a time like that? There was no need for words. We were together and we shared that moment as friends, drawing strength from one another, grappling with the twin demons of anger and sadness with all of our combined courage. It was an evening I'll never forget and a coalescing of souls that I will never fully understand.

After a few more days of tests, John started weeks of chemotherapy. He was frail and sallow when he was finally able to come home, but he was awfully happy to be there.

On the first Saturday after he came home, an absolutely amazing thing happened. Looking back, I know that it was more than just amazing. It was a miracle.

I don't remember how it started, whose idea it was, or how it got so well organized so quickly. But one way or another, all of John's friends came over to his house that day. Some brought lumber. Others brought tools. Some brought only the sweat they could generate, while others brought food and drink to keep the workers going. In the space of one incredible day, with no advance planning and no real idea of how to go about it, John's many friends celebrated their love for this gentle man by having an old-fashioned workshop-raising.

In just eight hours, a motley crew of rank amateurs designed, built, wired, painted, and christened a new storage shed and workshop to replace the one that the state was taking. By nightfall, all of John's tools and projects were in place. During the course of that remarkable day, we worked together, sipped lemonade and ate fried chicken together, laughed together at our collective ineptness, and prayed together for the good health of the friend who had blessed us all.

I can't even begin to describe the feelings. Big John cried like a baby. Come to think of it, we all did.

A few days later John went back into the hospital. We visited him almost daily. On Sundays, our minister, Joe Holder, held impromptu services in John's room for any family and friends who cared to gather there. John choreographed those services, and they were a sight. We sang together, prayed together, and even laid on hands and prayed for healing. In our desperate desire to help our friend, we divested ourselves of all of the inhibitions that had always stood between us and true communion with God. We must have been a sight to anyone who happened by and looked in the door.

One night I went alone to John's room. No one else was there. I immediately sensed that he was different, and I was right. He talked with a resolve I hadn't heard before.

He told me that he was going to die and that he knew it. He told me that Jesus had come to him, not in a dream, but while he was awake, right there in his room. He said that Jesus had sat there on the end of his bed and had told him that he was going to die, but that it was as it was supposed to be, and that everything would be all right. John said all of that without a trace of hesitation and with complete conviction. I believed it then, and I believe it now.

After that, John let go. He seemed content to let his life run its course, and he spent much of his time trying to help the rest of us understand. As for me, while I grieved mightily, I let go, too. The anxiety receded somewhat, but the anger did not. Those were long, dark days.

On the twenty-sixth of May, I stopped by the hospital. I was on my way home after a three-day trip. I was tired, but it wouldn't take a minute just to pop in and say hello.

No one was there. The bed was empty and freshly changed. There was no sign that John had ever been in that room.

I stood in the middle of the room and let my feelings rush over me. Grief, relief, gratitude, anger—all were there in abundance. Then I dropped to my knees and prayed a prayer of thanksgiving. I thanked God for Big John and for Jesus Christ, who assured us that even in death everything can be all right.

More than twenty years have passed since that day, but Big John is still my friend. He touched me in a special way and created a place for himself in my heart. He's still there, too.

John taught me a lot about life and how to live it. He taught me even more about death and how to face it.

Was it an accident that John changed jobs that January, making a career move so totally out of character? By doing so, he acquired group insurance that paid all the expenses of his illness and provided life insurance for Judy and Jonathan. In his old job, his benefits had been far, far less.

Was it an accident that the best doctors in Nashville failed in November and December to see a tumor that was as big as a silver dollar by the next March? The tumor was discovered only two weeks after the policy went into effect. Because of that, the preexisting conditions clause in his new insurance policy did not preclude coverage.

Did Jesus really visit John?

In the ninth chapter of the Gospel of John, Jesus touched the eyes of a blind man and restored his sight. That man had a simple answer when his detractors asked him if Jesus had actually performed a miracle. "One thing do I know," he said. "I was blind, but now I see." Well, I don't know what happened in Big John's room that night. One thing do I know, however. John was dying and he was torn by grief and fear. After that night, he faced death with the serenity of one who knew the truth.

John Waddey Roberts lived a life of honor, truth, and integrity. He never acquired wealth and he never knew fame. Yet, when he was buried, his gravesite was surrounded by people whose lives were richer because he had been their friend. He was, in all the right ways, a very big man.

Thanks, Big John.

THE MOST IMPORTANT CONVERSATION OF ALL

When my son Richard was eleven, he decided to go out for the football team at the school where he was enrolling for the first time. He was to be a fifth grader.

Richard didn't know much about football at the time. This was to be his first experience with the game. But that didn't seem to bother him a bit. He was blessed with one of the great self-images of all times. He honestly believed he could do whatever he wanted to do. Besides, most of his friends were going out for the team. That was all the incentive he needed.

It turned out to be a long, long season.

Oh, the practices were all right. During practice he learned the game from the ground up. But during the games he languished on the sidelines, watching the other fellows play. He kept on smiling, however, always confident that his chance would come, always determined to be ready.

The sum total of his season was a single appearance, in the last game, for the very last play. On that play he just stood there and watched the action unfold in front of him while I captured the historic event, or non-event, with my home movie camera. His spotless jersey was easy to find. When the whistle blew ending the game, he trotted off with his sweat-soaked teammates.

He told me later it was a very special moment for him.

When the next season rolled around, he was filled with excitement. "This year I'm going to make the second string," he told me one August day, and he said it with unabashed pride and determination.

It can be tough on a dad when his son aspires to nothing greater than the second team. That's the perfect time for a parental speech. You know the one; it's all about setting high goals and not settling for second best or selling yourself short.

Fortunately, the urge passed.

Our children seldom benefit from the things we tell them anyway. Unsolicited advice may be heard, but it rarely makes it to the heart. My words would have been wasted. He wasn't looking for advice. He was simply sharing his excitement, and I was lucky enough to be nearby. I didn't spoil it. In an uncharacteristic burst of wisdom, I managed to keep my mouth shut.

I drove him over to the school on the first day of practice that year. He was barely able to sit still.

"You're really looking forward to this, aren't you, Richard?" I asked.

"I sure am," came the reply. "I like practice best of all, 'cause that's when I get to scrimmage and try out all of the fancy things."

"All I remember about August football practice is the blocking and tackling," I mused.

"Yeah, I know," he responded, his smile fading. "I wish we could skip all that and go on to the fun stuff. I learned to block and tackle last year."

Once again the urge hit me. Once again I let it pass.

Skip the basics and go on to the fun stuff. Isn't that how we would all like to approach our lives?

In a young child it isn't surprising to hear such an idea. Yet in truth, the people who succeed, the ones who rise to the top in any endeavor, are the ones who have been soundly schooled in the fundamentals, but who nonetheless keep working on them over and over. The winners are the ones who have a solid foundation on which to build, the ones who know who they are and where they are going.

What's true of life is true also of faith.

We who profess to be Christians must have a solid foundation. We must be certain about the fundamentals of our faith. We must go back to the basics time and time again. We must go back to the roots of our faith and be certain that our lives are still grounded in the solid soil of belief in Jesus Christ as our savior. Only then can we get fancy. Only then can we deal with human emotion, human problems, social issues, and the myriad of topics that form the vast smorgasbord of human experience. All of that is sound and fury, signifying nothing, if our foundation is not solid and unshakable.

Well, that incident with Richard came and went, and I forgot about it until several years later, when my oldest daughter, Barby, turned sixteen.

Being male, I have no idea what it must be like to be a girl and turn sweet sixteen. It must be special, though.

I have seen it happen twice from a father's perspective, and I can tell you that a magical transformation occurs. No matter what has happened before, no matter how grown-up your daughter thought she was before, when she passes that sixteenth milestone she takes a giant step into the future. A father can only stand by and watch, smiling proudly, doing his best to hide his sadness and his fear. All he can do is hope and pray that his daughter is properly schooled in the basics, so that she can glide smoothly and safely through "the fun stuff" just ahead.

I thought about a lot of things on Barby's special birthday. Some of them made me sad. I felt that I hadn't been the father I had hoped to be. I probably hadn't lived up to her expectations. I know I hadn't lived up to mine.

What had I expected? I don't know. I guess I had always hoped to be something of a lovable friend, an omnipresent dispenser of worldly wisdom. I had hoped to be like those fathers you see on television—easy-going, impervious to life's ups and downs, arriving home every day at a predictable hour, donning slippers and sweater and sinking into a comfortable chair as the sun sinks lower in the western sky, discussing the day's events with attentive, devoted children who would hang on my every word.

It didn't happen.

I had hoped to be a confidant, a friend to whom they could turn, someone with whom they could share their innermost thoughts. I had even envisioned their friends coming to me for fatherly advice or for parental companionship, drawn to my side by the warmth of our home and by my reputation for patience and understanding.

That didn't happen, either.

Too often, what my children got was the leftovers. What they got was an excuse or an apology because once again, something had come up. Too often, their reaching out was greeted by a flip answer, an unwanted solution, or a response laced with misdirected hostility.

To be sure, it wasn't all negative. I had done a lot of things right as a father. But as I watched Barby take her first tentative steps into womanhood, the melancholy nature of that passage obscured my vision. I forgot the good and remembered only that I hadn't communicated with her as often, or as well, as I had wanted to. I felt a keen sense of loss. I hadn't played my part as well as I wished.

I spent a lot of time with my children, perhaps more than most. We had fun together. I'm grateful for that. Barbara more than made up for my shortcomings. Many a night I slipped off to sleep, while down the hall, behind a closed door, Barbara and one of the children were communicating in ways that only patience and practice could produce.

Barbara seemed to know instinctively that the key to

communicating with children is to be ready when *they* are ready and to be willing to listen as long as they are willing to talk. I just never got it. The time was never right. Patience was always lacking. There always seemed to be a mysterious barrier between us.

As I watched Barby blow out the sixteen candles, I asked myself a question. Is the foundation in place?

Christian parents have an awesome responsibility. God entrusts us with the care and nurture of his most precious possessions. It is up to us to lay the foundation. On that special day I could not possibly have cared more about anything than I did about Barby. I cared deeply about her spiritual development, and yet I had said so little.

My children knew I was a Christian, I suppose, but did they know why? They knew that I believed, but did they know what? I had tried, but the parent in me had always gotten in the way. Talking had always sounded like preaching. Explaining had always turned to exhortation. Plain language had always given way to pomposity. Self-consciousness had always choked off meaningful communication.

I was sad. Barby was sixteen, and we had never had the most important conversation of all.

It wasn't too late, though. With God's help, I found a way. I used the gift God had given me instead of dwelling on the absence of the gifts I didn't have. I wrote about it. I reached her the best way I knew how. I created on paper the conversation we had never been able to have in real life.

Here, with her permission, is that conversation. It was written for Barby and also for Lindy and Richard. It was written for all children and for all parents who believe strongly and care deeply, but who haven't been able to put it into words.

———

"Daddy, what do you believe?"

Well, first and foremost, I believe in God. I believe he

exists in some form, in someplace, and that his hand is in everything we see here on earth. And I believe that after I die, after everyone dies, there is another existence to which the spirit goes. In that existence, it is possible to have contact not only with God, but also with the people we have loved on earth.

"How can you believe something like that when it's impossible to know whether you're right or not?"

There are many answers, but the most important one is this: I believe, because in light of my experience, my mind and heart cannot encompass or accept any alternative.

You see, I have seen the miracle of nature. I have seen the first shoots of green burst through the barren ground, then grow and flourish without our help, later to flower into a spectrum of light and color that captures the spirit and dazzles the eye.

I have seen the miracle of birth. Where there was nothing, suddenly there is the most complex and fascinating little human being. I have seen it three times, with three of you. Each of you has your own spirit, your own will, your own heart beating as if by some mysterious signal, on and on in perfect rhythm. All your mother and I did was love each other. All the doctor did was slap your bottom. The rest is nothing short of a miracle.

I have also seen the miracle of death. I have seen the spirit and essence of humanness depart from the body and leave it cold and lifeless. That spirit then begins a journey to some unknown destination, to a level of reality unavailable to us on earth. I don't know where it goes, but as surely as I live and breathe, I have seen the trip begin.

I have seen and felt the wonder of God's spirit at work in my own life in ways that I can neither explain nor defend, but in ways that I know are real and true.

I have felt love, that indescribable feeling of warmth and excitement and satisfaction that fills your soul when another human being touches you and cares for you.

We do not create these things. We can't, and we don't.

All of our total creations, since the beginning of time, were made with materials that were already here when we arrived, using the bodies and brains we were given. All of the total knowledge we possess still cannot describe, explain, or duplicate the beauty of a rose kissed by dew, illuminated by morning sunlight.

The good things of life are not random accidents. They didn't just evolve. In the picture of our creation and in the world in which we live, there is an unmistakable imprint. The hand of a master painter has been here.

God loves us, and he wants us to enjoy all of this. He loves us enough to let us use it as his stewards. He loves us enough to sacrifice his own Son for our sake.

"Then you do believe in Jesus, Daddy? You really do believe he lived, and that he was God's son?"

Yes, I do.

I wasn't there. I haven't touched his nail-scarred hands or seen the wound in his side. But when the Bible assures me that "God so loved the world that he gave his only begotten Son," something deep inside me responds. Somewhere deep in my soul, that soul which is akin to the very spirit of God and is made in his image, a responsive chord is struck and an affirming "Amen" resounds. I know, as surely as I know myself, that this is true.

I believe that a part of God's spirit is in me and is part of me. When God created my soul and sent it on its journey to earth, his spirit was his gift to me. I have it, you have it, we all have it.

"But Daddy, don't you ever have doubts?"

Of course I do. Of course I do.

A dear friend once told me that for him, faith was believing in possibilities. Doubts are a necessary part of faith. Everyone has them.

You see, there are two ways to perceive, understand, and accept things. One is to know, and the other is to believe. Believing is accepting something as true without ever being able to actually know whether it is or not. That's what God has asked us to do. He has asked us to believe, to accept him at his word, although we cannot possibly *know* the truth with certainty as long as we are here on earth.

It would be easy to accept the reality of God and Jesus if it were possible to actually, logically, physically *know*. There would be no challenge, no choice, and no need for faith. Everyone would come aboard; there would be no such thing as nonbelievers. But it isn't that simple. God has asked us to have faith in the unknowable, and when imperfect humans try to do that, doubts naturally follow. To know is easy. To believe in spite of doubts is harder.

There is a story in the Bible that speaks to this. It's in the ninth chapter of Mark.

It's the story of a father who brought his young son to Jesus. The boy was gripped with a spirit. The biblical description is graphic and heart-rending. It sounds like a severe case of what we would call epilepsy.

The father had asked the disciples to cure it, and they had failed. That failure had just taken place when Jesus approached.

The father was at the end of his rope. "If you can do anything, have pity on us and help us," he said to Jesus.

Jesus seemed to be angry. "*If* you can!" he repeated. "All things are possible to him who believes."

At this, the father cried out from the depths of his despair. "I believe," he said. "Help my unbelief!"

Think about what it had to be like for that father. He would have done *anything* to bring relief to his son. He declared his faith, but at the same time admitted his humanity and acknowledged his doubts. He asked for Jesus' help as an imperfect human.

Jesus answered his prayer. He didn't rebuke the man for his doubts. Instead, he drove the spirit out of the man's son.

Like that father, we are human. We cannot deny our humanity or hide our doubts behind a false bravado. Our doubts will always be there. All we can do is pray for the strength we need in order to believe in spite of them.

"Daddy, I know you pray. Do you believe that God really hears and answers prayer?"

Yes. I believe God hears and answers prayer.

In the seventh chapter of Matthew, Jesus tells me to ask for what I need and promises me that I will receive it. I have done that. I have prayed, and I have seen and known God's answer. I have felt the touch of God in my life in response to prayer.

I cannot describe it, and I cannot possibly explain it, but I have experienced it. I urge you to find out for yourself. In the twenty-first chapter of Matthew, Jesus promises that "whatever you ask in prayer, you will receive, if you have faith." Pray as often as you can, believing that your prayers will be answered.

"But Daddy, why does God answer some prayers, and not answer others?"

I don't know. That's a tough one.

Sometimes we don't have the faith we need. We don't truly believe that our prayers will be answered. I know that has been true for me.

Sometimes when I pray, I ask God to search my heart and know where I really am and what I really need. But sometimes I know what I want, and nothing else will do. I present God not only with a problem, but with the solution that I want as well. When I do that, I run the risk of rejecting any other response, or of missing God's response entirely, because it isn't what I asked for. When I do that, I limit God's ability to perform a miracle in my life.

I believe that God answers prayer but that we humans don't always hear the answer. The problem isn't in the message, it is in the listener.

"You keep referring to the Bible, Daddy. Did God write it? Is it really his word?"

I believe that every single word of the Bible was divinely inspired.

"Is every single word literally true?"

I don't know. Many people of faith argue about this point, feeling quite strongly one way or the other. I simply don't know. I have never seen anyone accomplish anything worthwhile by arguing about matters of faith that cannot be known with certainty.

The important thing to me is that what I need in life is in that book. The principles for living well are there, as are the seeds of faith. It is more than just a book. When I read it, my spirit is being lifted in a special way.

I am certain of this: the Bible is the Living Word. There is power in its pages. To get that power, I have to read it. If I don't find what I need, the fault is mine. The Bible is alive. I am more alive when I read it.

"Daddy, if there is a loving God, and if he really loves every one of us, then why does he let tragedy happen?"

That may be the hardest question of all. Many an anguished human has railed out in anger at the loss of a loved one, venting emotion at what seems like a dispassionate, uncaring God.

Why does tragedy strike families who live in faith and are devoted to God?

Why do people die in the prime of their lives, even while leading exemplary lives and believing in God?

Why do people who literally glow with faith and love sometimes find themselves crippled and stricken with painful, debilitating diseases?

There is much unfairness in this world. Good people suffer. Why does a loving God permit that to happen?

Perhaps the answer lies in one of God's most important gifts to humankind. That gift is freedom.

We are free, free to choose, free to believe or not believe, free to accept or not accept both the gift of salvation and the presence of the kingdom of God on earth. This freedom enables us to experience fully the beauty of the moment when the right decision is made, the freewill decision of faith.

But we are also free to act in haste, to make bad decisions, to do the wrong thing. And because we are free, things can happen that may not seem right or fair or just. If God routinely interfered in the course of everyday life, that freedom would be gone, and with it would be gone the choice to have faith and the ability to accept God's gifts.

God doesn't want bad things to happen. He doesn't want bad choices to be made. I believe a tear rolls down God's cheek when one of his children suffers. God cares, but God created us to be free.

In the eighth chapter of Romans, Paul assures us that "in everything God works for good, with those who love him, who are called according to his purpose." I believe those words are true; I believe it with all my heart. All I can do is to keep on having faith in the omnipresence of his love, and keep on believing that he really does care what happens to every one of us.

WILLIE THE WEEPER

This particular adventure began when Barbara and I decided to move ourselves and our three children, who were then quite small, into an old two-story white house. It had been in the same family for thirty-three years prior to our buying it, and for the last eight of those years it had been occupied by two elderly sisters, one of whom had the unlikely name of "Cherry Orchard." Involved as they were with their plants and their memories, keeping hardwood floors waxed and woodwork scrubbed hadn't been a high priority. We faced a monumental cleanup.

One day I was muttering about our problem within earshot of Henry Goodpasture, the senior partner in the law firm where I worked. Mister Henry, as he was fondly called, heard my distress. Moreover, he had a ready solution.

"Now you tell Barbara," he said in his engaging Southern style, "that I'm going to send my man over to help her out. When she gets through with him, tell her to send him back." That was the sum and substance of it. No explanation, no inquiry as to whether we wanted his "man" or not, just a declarative statement, said with the innocence of one offering to lend a favorite book or a useful tool. I felt a bit awkward as he said it, and I barely responded at all.

Awkward or not, I mentioned Mr. Goodpasture's offer to Barbara that night. It sounded like a pretty good idea to her. Several days passed, however, and nothing more was said. Both my discomfort and the notion of actually getting this unexpected help finally drifted into the background. I spent my days practicing law and my nights and weekends helping Barbara scrub away at the accumulated grime of the ages. Armed with the enthusiasm of youth and the motivation of poverty, we chipped away at the task, one backbreaking room at a time. Then it happened.

One sunny day, without fanfare, there appeared at our back door a diminutive black man, smiling broadly, riding a bicycle, carrying nothing but a paper sack full of clothes and a mayonnaise jar full of chicken fat. Willie the Weeper had arrived.

To know and understand Willie the Weeper, you have to also know a little about Henry and Virginia Goodpasture—Mister Henry and Miss Virginia.

Henry Goodpasture was small in stature. He had a pink face that turned strawberry red when he was excited, a mane of solid white hair, and a deceptive look of dignity that soon gave way to the devilish imp that lurked within. He was quiet, soft-spoken, well-mannered, and articulate, the last of a vanishing breed of Southern gentry. Miss Virginia was a lady of great style and charm. She would have been perfectly in place gliding down the spiral stairs at Charleston's Drayton Hall, welcoming guests and putting servants at ease with her gracious manner.

It would be possible, I suppose, for one to be offended by Mister Henry's reference to Willie as his "man." Indeed, this was the very response that had made me feel awkward when he first mentioned it. I soon realized, however, that to suffer such offense, one would have to read into it something that simply wasn't there. Mister Henry didn't have a demeaning bone in his body. When he referred to Willie as his man, he did so in the most generous sense of that phrase. Both he and Willie were sons of the early twentieth-century South. They were tied together by bonds that I would never know or understand, bonds that somehow transcended the passage of time and the shifting of attitudes. By the time I met Willie, their relationship was something that I hadn't created and couldn't possibly change. When Mister Henry offered to lend him to me, it was an act of kindness.

Willie first started working for Mister Henry in 1931, when the Goodpastures lived in a house not a mile away from the one we were trying to clean up. He stayed with them from 1931 to 1944 at that location. In 1945, the Goodpastures bought a beautiful antebellum house on two hundred rolling acres fifteen miles south of Nashville. For the next thirty years that's where Willie lived, when he chose to stay in one place.

Willie the Weeper was in his upper sixties when he came to us. That was Mister Henry's best guess, anyway. In truth, he was ageless. He stood well under five feet tall. His skin was a rich, deep mahogany, and his arms bulged with muscles built up over decades of toil. He had a small, shiny bald head and perpetually watery eyes, which more or less accounted for his nickname. His face bore a striking resemblance to one of Walt Disney's seven dwarfs. His clothes looked like something Goodwill might have rejected. He was quite a sight, standing on our back steps, waiting for instructions.

Mister Henry had told me that Willie was a prodigious worker, but in reality, that was an understatement. He had said that Willie was childlike in many respects and required a great deal of supervision, but that was also an understatement. He had said of Willie that if you told him to dig a ditch and left him alone to do it, Willie would soon dig through your property and start turning your neighbor's soil. That particular admonition was a fore-shadowing of things to come.

On Willie's first Saturday at our house, he and I were standing near a long block wall that the former owners had built right down the middle of the backyard. I asked Willie if he thought he could knock the wall down for me. I hadn't decided to do that yet; I was just thinking about it. Willie smiled and said he thought he could probably handle it. I went off to do something else, thinking nothing more about it. When I came back a few minutes later, Willie was beaming proudly. A ten-foot section of wall lay at his feet!

Barbara soon discovered that she also had to be very specific with Willie or else he would start thinking up tasks on his own, without regard as to whether he knew how to do them. She had trouble getting used to that, and apparently Willie had an equally difficult time getting used to her.

One day Barbara decided that she and Willie would clean out a patch of honeysuckle that had invaded our backyard. She explained the task to him, handed him a pair of clippers, then tore into the job herself. She was soon obscured by flying pieces of chopped honeysuckle. Minutes later, she realized that Willie was still standing there, motionless, mouth gaping open, clippers hanging limply from his hand.

"What's the matter, Willie?" Barbara asked.

"Miss Virginia, she just points," Willie replied.

Willie took great pride in his work. He loved to be praised and affirmed. Like most of us, he wanted to actually hear the words. Unlike many of us, when words of praise didn't come his way, he went after them. He would finish a particular task, come get me, lead me to the site of his work, point to it silently, and flash his impish grin. Then he'd roll up his sleeve, flex the prominent muscle in his stubby arm, and deliver his favorite one-liner.

"Mister Henry done sent you the wrong man!"

I soon learned that the only acceptable response was, "Oh no, Willie. You've done a wonderful job. Mister Henry definitely sent me the right man!"

Willie's one-liner is still a part of our family tradition.

Willie stayed with us for several days. We provided his room and board, but he wouldn't even consider our invitations to sit at our table. This created a dilemma for Barbara and me, caught up as we were in the new liberality of the early seventies. Willie preferred to do his own thing. He would simply take his food and a large bottle of Tabasco sauce, which he poured on everything he ate, and sit on the back porch or under a tree. After a while, we quit fretting about it. Willie was the product of another era. Our protestations only made him feel uncomfortable.

Willie slept in our basement on an old mattress turned into a makeshift bed. We had offered him a couch in the den, but again he had refused. The basement was the only place left, and he made it clear that this was what he preferred. Years later, our oldest daughter's chief memory of Willie was how sorry she felt because he slept in the basement. We felt sorry, too.

Willie never talked about how long he expected to stay. Each evening he would disappear into the basement; each morning he would emerge, ready to work. Then one day, without warning or discussion, he pumped up the tires on his old bicycle and rode away. Barbara and I had a long list of unfinished projects, but that didn't matter. It was as if some internal clock had told him that it was time for him to move on. We hadn't seen the last of Willie, though. Not by a long shot. Willie was the personification of loyalty. Once you had him, he was as much your man as he was anyone else's.

Mister Henry had warned me about that, too. He told me that when the great blizzard of 1951 hit Nashville, Willie was in East Nashville, visiting a half-brother. When the big freeze hit in the middle of the night, Willie was so worried about the Goodpastures that he actually walked the fifteen-plus miles out to the country place and had a roaring fire going in the old coal furnace before the family had gotten out of bed.

We soon became the objects of Willie's loyalty. After a while a routine developed. Willie would show up at our back door, bike, paper sack, chicken fat and all. The chicken fat was another of his trademarks. He always carried an ample supply, which he used to season his food. Every time he showed up, Barbara found something for him to do, lest he misdo something else. When he was ready to leave, he left, whether he was through or not.

Every now and then Willie visited my law office. Most of the time it was because he needed money. Acting on Mr. Henry's instructions, I paid Willie by putting his money in a bank account and giving it to him when he asked for it. This was an arrangement that was in its thirtieth year when I first met him, and it seemed to suit him fine. Thus at odd times he would come by, unannounced, wanting some of his money. He always showed up when the reception area was filled with dignified, well-dressed clients in search of serious legal advice.

I can still picture him sitting there, incongruously ensconced in a Chippendale armchair, wearing hand-me-down clothes, a rope for a belt, a scarf tied atop his little bald head, sporting a big, broad smile that split his face like a bright quarter moon on a dark brown sky. That was Willie. Always ready with a loud, boisterous greeting and a friendly smile, no matter where he was or what was going on around him.

As time passed, Willie acquired the friendship of an old stray dog who became his sidekick. During those days we were seeing less and less of him at our house. We never saw the dog in person, but apparently Willie, his dog, and his fully loaded bicycle were a familiar sight on the streets of Nashville. To our delight, his picture appeared in the newspaper one day, together with a nice little article about this friendly, modern-day gypsy and his faithful companion. I'll never forget that picture of Willie and his dog, nor will I forget Willie's pride as he talked about that sudden burst of fame.

One winter day, Willie showed up in our office with a government check for five hundred dollars made out to himself. He gave it to our bookkeeper, then he disappeared. We held that check for a few days, trying to find out where it had come from. Willie wasn't on any kind of pension, he hadn't retired from anything, he hadn't applied for welfare, and Mister Henry's efforts to sign him up for Social Security had proven fruitless since he'd never held a job where anyone had withheld anything. Finally we just deposited the check and went on about our business. No doubt Willie would be coming by for cash any day.

But he didn't. We didn't see him again. Then the call came. The police had found the body of one William Hunter, black male, age unknown, huddled in a downtown doorway. There was no sign of the bicycle or the dog.

Willie had frozen to death. Apparently he had fallen victim to some of the predators that lurk the streets of our cities. Nowhere to go and too badly hurt to try, Willie lay alone in a sheltered doorway and slowly died of exposure. The only link between Willie and the rest of civilization was a scrap of our law firm stationery that was found in his pocket. That's why the police had called us. Did we know this William Hunter?

The sudden, shocking revelation of the true identity of Willie the Weeper was a sharp blow to my self-righteous gut. Sure, my family loved him, and I'd been good to him in many respects. But somehow I'd lost sight of who he was and what he was. I had freely used his strength, but had taken his humanity so lightly. William Hunter. This kind little man, about whom we had spoken with such casual indifference, was William Hunter. There had been a mother and a father, perhaps some brothers and sisters.

There had been a childhood filled with laughter and tears and a lifetime of devotion and hard work. I was ashamed that I had acknowledged his dignity only in death.

Did we know this William Hunter? Sadly we admitted that we did, and the small, brown body became our responsibility.

We carried Willie, the five hundred dollars, and an old suit to a funeral parlor and negotiated for the best service we could afford. A few days later we all filed awkwardly into the little chapel, strangers in an alien territory, come to pay our last respects to a dear old friend.

It was my first black funeral. Several minutes slipped by before I felt comfortable with the singing, the hand-clapping, and the testimonials uttered by some of the well-meaning strangers in attendance that day. I later learned that most of them were paid mourners who didn't really know our Willie. It was an interesting irony, since Willie's nickname had originally belonged to a young lad in a Dickens novel who earned his keep by shedding tears and mourning loudly for total strangers.

After the testimonials were over there was a pause. The preacher asked if we wanted to "pass." I recovered from my ignorance and joined the line of mourners walking slowly along in front of the open coffin.

Willie looked as uncomfortable as I felt. He was too clean, too shiny. The suit and tie were adjusted mannequin perfect, but they really weren't Willie. And the perpetual smile was gone forever. Cleaned up for perhaps the first time in many years, Willie was a sad sight for my newly sensitive eyes.

The old black preacher began the eulogy. He, too, was a hired stranger, but I remember the poignant beauty of his opening words to this very day. He was almost a caricature of himself as he held tightly to the lectern and rocked back on his heels, belting out his words in rumbling, sonorous tones that echoed off of the bare walls of the chapel.

"Now, I didn't have the privilege of knowing the late Mister Hunter," he began. "I am certain that he was, in this life, a fine man. But whatever he was, I know for sure that he is now at home with his Maker, walking along those golden streets, somewhere beyond the purple hills of time."

"Amen," I whispered. "Amen."

In the twenty-fifth chapter of Matthew, Jesus tells us that when the Son of man comes in his glory, he's going to separate the sheep from the goats. The sheep will join him in glory, beyond those purple hills of time. But the goats aren't going to understand. They're going to cry out in anguish, wondering where they went wrong. The answer will be damningly simple. Every time they insulted, discounted, demeaned, or ignored the least of their brethren, they did it to Jesus Christ himself. Every single time.

By most standards, Willie the Weeper was one of the least. But he was, in fact, one of the brethren. He was a child of God, and his life was a gift from God to all who knew him. In God's eyes, the least are every bit as beautiful and every bit as important as the greatest. Whoever believes in him shall have eternal life, and that "whoever" includes us all.

God loves all of his children, regardless of education, experience, nationality, the tint of the skin, the shape of the head, the slant of the eyes, the size of the lips, or any other of those characteristics which seem so important to us. It is inconsistent with a Christian faith to believe anything else.

All of God's children are born with his spirit already in their hearts, and with his love for them already assured. This is the essence of being human. All men and women are God's children, and all are equally entitled to be treated with respect and to be accorded a measure of dignity. All of them. Even Willie the Weeper.

That realization was Willie's gift to me.

CHRISTOPHER SNIDER
GOES OUT TO PLAY

On Easter Sunday, March 26, 1749, in a cabin somewhere in rural North Carolina, attended only by family members and a friend, a woman gave birth to a baby boy. The cabin had one room and a dirt floor. It was warmed by a blazing fire; steam was rising from a cauldron of boiling water. A caring attendant was on hand, as was a concerned husband, but there was no doctor. In 1749 in rural North Carolina, the birth experience was primitive, lonely, and frightening.

The mother was only sixteen, but it wasn't at all unusual for one so young to be giving birth. Her husband was somewhat older, but not a great deal. On the North Carolina frontier, women married very young.

In this primitive wilderness, miscarriages and still-births were the rule, not the exception. Fewer than half of the conceived children were born alive; fewer than half of those ever reached adulthood. The odds were discouraging. In spite of the odds, however, a boy was born, bellowing out his first complaint. The weary young mother lapsed into sleep; the father beamed with pride, as though his presence had actually been of some help. Thus it was that Jacob Blount and Barbara Gray Blount became parents. William Blount was on his way to the pages of history.

William Blount lived for fifty years. That was a fairly long life for the times. His was an eventful life, too. He distinguished himself as a planter and landowner and became wealthy. He served in the North Carolina Militia, was an Indian agent, and later became a politician. He served in the Continental Congress and was the first territorial administrator of the land called Tennessee. When that territory became a state, he was one of its first two senators. He was later expelled from the Senate for his involvement in a plot to use the British Navy and Native American Indians to conquer what is now Florida, which proves conclusively that neither Watergate nor Olliegate was anything new. We have always been willing to place the end ahead of the means.

Jacob and Barbara Gray Blount beat the odds again three years later, in 1752, when John Gray Blount was born. He, too, lived more than fifty years and was likewise a landowner and planter of some renown, as well as a North Carolina Assemblyman and a soldier in the Revolutionary War. He was also a younger brother, a fact that was to be of some significance to me personally, even though more than two hundred years would pass before I would be born.

During his lifetime, Jacob Blount accumulated some land in the southeastern part of North Carolina, which he left to his boys upon his death. Land was the principle medium of wealth back then, and being able to make it produce was vitally important. Both boys knew this. The future of the family depended upon the successful operation of the family land. The future was secure as long as they worked hard. The brothers did so quite willingly.

In 1787, opportunity knocked. William and John Gray Blount were both invited to represent North Carolina at the Constitutional Convention in Philadelphia. Both wanted to go, but the risks were too great. Travel was hazardous, and no one could predict what turmoil might surround the convention itself. Someone had to stay with the land.

It was decided that William Blount would go. He would take the risk upon his broad shoulders. John Gray Blount, the obedient younger brother, would keep the homeplace together for future generations.

The choice of a replacement was not left up to chance. It was, in fact, left up to John Gray Blount himself. He chose another prominent North Carolina planter, his long-time friend Richard Dobbs Spaight. This is how it came about that my name, albeit spelled a bit differently, appears on the United States Constitution.

Historical trivia like this isn't worth a great deal in the marketplace, of course, but isn't it interesting?

It is important to have a little knowledge of history. I know that now.

If I had it all to do over again, I'd definitely study more history in school. I just didn't get the message. I thought the point was to pass, not to learn. To me, history was just a lot of dates and names and the endless torture of memorization. It was something to be endured, not absorbed.

It wasn't the fault of my teachers. Two of the teachers whom I remember most fondly from high school—Stuart Nicholson and John Younger, Sr.—tried their best to show me the error of my ways. Unfortunately, they couldn't penetrate my teenaged defenses. It never occurred to me that the pages of history were populated with real people, or that I might learn something about life by looking at the way those real people lived. As I've grown older I've come to appreciate the past more and more and to understand that the wisdom of life is accumulated and tempered over the ages, not re-invented by each succeeding generation.

The loss was mine. History isn't just dates and events. It's people and their interaction with one another. It's the impact that their actions had upon the world they lived in and the impact those same actions still have on the world in which I live. It's the lessons we can learn and the choices we have because of what other people did

51

many years ago. History is important. It's alive. It's fascinating.

Sometimes the most fascinating events in history are the ones that were seemingly small and insignificant at the time. The tapestry of history contains millions of threads, and at the time when any single one is being woven into place, it isn't always possible to know just how important it may be. The story of Christopher Snider is one such small thread, a single brief event that had a profound, cumulative impact on the world, an impact that continues today.

In the winter of 1770, Christopher Snider was twelve years old, living in Boston with his parents. Boston was a growing town, a bustling center of commerce and activity, with about twenty-five thousand permanent inhabitants and heaven only knows how many transients. It was a seaport, and its streets were full of the sounds of frenetic activity even on a snowy February day.

Plagued by growth and haunted by success, Boston was a crowded place. Narrow streets were rutted with muddy tracks; tiny buildings were jammed together, their second floors jutting out over the roadways in many places. Houses were small, roughhewn, and squeezed together; living conditions were difficult at best. Several family members often slept together in a tiny room. But in places like Boston, in times like those, people made the best of their situations, living together and loving one another, trying their best to carve out an existence.

On this particular blustery February day, Christopher Snider's mother was somewhat exasperated, looking for her son.

"Christopher Snider, where do you think you're going?" Her voice pierced the winter silence and bounced off of the wooden walls of the small room. Christopher stopped in midstep, halfway out of the door. He turned instinctively toward the sound of his mother's voice.

"Out to play," he said, not timidly, but not rudely,

either. He knew better than to be rude to his mother. She wasn't the type who would take kindly to such behavior, especially from her twelve-year-old son.

Christopher's mother stood in the center of the small room, hands on hips, still clutching the towel she had been using to wipe out the heavy pottery bowl that had held their lunch minutes earlier. As she watched her son come back inside and close the door behind himself, a trace of a smile tugged upwardly at the corners of her mouth.

She couldn't help smiling when she saw her son. It was involuntary; a reflection of the warm wellspring of love that invariably arose within her at times like this. He was tall for his age, but not at all awkward or gangly. Hard work had molded his arms and chest with manly crispness; a good spirit had carved pleasant features on his freckled face. An unruly mop of sandy hair crowned his head. It was this exposed thatch that concerned his mother. He was bundled well enough in his warm woolen coat, and his gloves were hanging out of one of the pockets. His boots were laced, and his scarf was in its place around his shoulders. But what about his head? He'd catch his death of cold!

"Where's your cap?" she asked.

He didn't answer, but glanced furtively at the row of hooks on the wall next to the doorway. One arm reached out like a lizard's tongue; one cap instantly found its way to his head. For good measure, he quickly wrapped the scarf around his neck before she had time to do it for him.

"Have you finished your chores?" she asked.

"Yes ma'am," he responded, ticking them off on his fingers. "The water barrel is full. I broke up the ice. The animals have all been fed. The wood is stacked. Everything has been done."

"Is your father going to need you this afternoon?"

"Yes ma'am," came the reply. "I'll be back. I promise. He said it was okay."

She put down the towel and stepped closer to her son. She pulled the cap down tighter onto his head, then tugged at the edges of the scarf, covering up a little more of his neck. Adjustments like these weren't needed necessarily, but she was a mother, and such adjustments were simply a part of what mothers did.

She touched his freshly scrubbed cheek with one hand, then drew it back.

"Be careful, honey," she said, as if her warning might make a difference. "And stay away from the Marketplace, whatever you do," she added.

"I will, Mom," he promised as he scurried away.

"I love you," she called out.

"You, too," he answered, unable to say "I love you." But he did love her, and she knew it.

She watched him bounce down the small wooden staircase. Her eyes followed him as he trudged across the narrow yard, through the gate, and on into the street beyond, being careful not to step into any of the squishy mud that was everywhere these days, careful, at least, when he was where she could still see him.

Once he was out of sight, she breathed a deep, contented sigh and closed the door.

There are some things that are constant throughout history, feelings and emotions that are present no matter what the time, the place, or the circumstances. Some of these constants are so hard to define that they have eluded the pens of poets and prophets for generations. They are there, they are real, and yet they defy the kind of description that would enable others to understand and empathize. They are, in short, universal feelings that are so unique that one who has not lived them cannot possibly know them. One of these, perhaps the most unique of all, is the love of a mother for a child.

Christopher Snider's mother was feeling that kind of love on that February day so long ago, the kind of love that would sacrifice even life itself, if that's what it took to see her child grown to manhood in good health. She was a real woman with a real son, living in a vital, real world in 1770. The love they felt for each other was real, indeed.

"Be careful, honey. And stay away from the Marketplace, whatever you do."

The Marketplace. The crossroads. The center of everything. The melting pot. The place where goods and ideas were exchanged in rapid fire, with tempers and emotions quickly rising to a boil. For this was a time of new ideas in Boston, radical ideas like freedom and representation and a voice in one's own destiny. Ideas that were shouted out in alehouses, where sons of liberty, fortified by strong drink, called for an end to tyranny; ideas that were whispered on street corners, where the dreaded Redcoats walked nearby, their crimson garb boldly defining their swaggering arrogance. The Marketplace. That's where the city was alive. A strong magnet for a young boy whose own father had spoken of freedom many times, though quietly, and only from the edges of the fray.

Out into the street he walked.

Where did he live? Perhaps Hancock Street, though that noble patriot had yet to inscribe his name so boldly that the King of England might read it with ease. Perhaps Washington Street, though the fate of a new land had yet to be placed in the hands of that strong leader. Perhaps Freedom Street, though freedom was still a dream, or State Street, though statehood was not yet an idea. Maybe it was near the first public school, or close to the meetinghouse where Patriots would someday gather, or on one of those streets where men would soon march with determination on their way to cast the tea into the harbor, thereby casting the shackles of bondage off of thousands of shoulders.

Where did he live? That part is no longer known. But it was Boston, and it was 1770, and Christopher Snider, age twelve, was going out to play. And sometime during the course of the afternoon it happened, as it so often does. He lost track of time and place and found himself where he wasn't supposed to be. The Marketplace.

Perhaps it was the shouting that drew him near. Perhaps it was the sound of horses' hooves or marching boots. Perhaps it was the sight of the crimson coats, the dreaded sight that raised the hackles on the back of his young neck.

Was his father there, somewhere in the crowd? What was going on? What was it that caught young Christopher's eye? Was it the British officer, the one swaggering about in the boastful, arrogant way of the oppressor in the midst of the oppressed? Was there an incident? Were words exchanged? What was so important that Christopher would disobey his mother?

That, too, is lost in history.

"Look at him," Christopher muttered under his breath as he stood on the edge of the crowd, looking across at the finely garbed officer.

"Listen to him," Christopher said almost audibly as he heard the officer's words escalate rapidly into commands. He hated the way the Redcoats pushed people around like so many nameless servants, using power as if it were theirs to keep instead of a sacred trust.

"How can he do that?" Christopher said out loud as his blood began to boil.

He didn't understand the issues. Not really. The bits and pieces he had overheard held some meaning, but not much.

"I hate him," he cried out, focusing his attention on the one causing all the trouble, the one with the gold braid on his shoulders and the tall hat perched on his head. The enemy, that's all he was to Christopher. Just another finely robed dandy in the scarlet cloth of England.

History has recorded precious little about what really happened that day, but what we know is this: On February

22, 1770, in the Marketplace in Boston, a twelve-year-old boy named Christopher Snider, filled with the reflected anger of his parents, did what he was born to do.

The tall hat and the gold braids were too much of a target. The February snow was too available. Quickly a handful was scooped up. Quickly it became a hardened ball. Quickly a strong young arm was cocked. Quickly his anger was focused at the enemy, with the only weapon at hand.

Christopher Snider rocked back on his heels and with a mighty heave, lurched forward into manhood, sending a frosty missile on its way. It found its mark. The hat went flying. Christopher stood his ground.

When the startled officer looked for his assailant, there stood young Christopher, his teeth tightly clenched, his jaw jutted outward. The tension of new excitement showed in his proud stance; the light of new freedom shone in his bright eyes. Such as it was, he had struck a blow against tyranny in the only way he knew how. The British officer, his pride and dignity destroyed, unholstered his pistol, took aim, and put a single bullet into Christopher's head, killing him instantly.

That bullet exploded inside Christopher's mother's heart, tearing it into tiny pieces. It cut a path across the pages of history, drawing a line, saying to the world that this was enough, that this was as far as the British dare go. It found its way into the hearts of Patriots everywhere, as word of this horrible, needless, inexcusable death spread like wildfire. Fourteen days later, and not very far away, five more men were killed in the Boston Massacre, and the revolution that gave birth to this country was under way.

Many would make incredible sacrifices for freedom before it was over. But the very first person to stand up and be counted, the first person to lay down his life for the country we cherish, was Christopher Snider, age twelve. His mother's tears flowed freely as his young and noble blood stained the streets of Boston with the hated red, fanning the small flame of freedom into a raging fire that would finally consume its enemy and light the path of liberty for millions of us who would someday follow.

WE'RE FROM WOODMONT!
COULDN'T BE PROUDER!

I know he meant well, this friend of mine, but frankly, I wish he had waited until after I finished the lesson.

It was a Sunday morning in April, and I had climbed the steep stairwell to the Challenge Class one more time. I was there to teach. As always, I was preoccupied with what I was about to do. The preceding hour had been filled with the usual insecurities that haunted me right before every lesson. Will it be okay? Will they like it? Will they get the point? *Is* there a point?

I sometimes wasted a good deal of time on that kind of arrogant nonsense instead of letting God take over.

Anyway, there I was, nervously single-minded about the coming presentation, when an old friend approached me and handed me a gaily wrapped, ribbon-bedecked package. It was so heavy that I almost dropped it. When I opened it, my jaw fell. It was a brick! A used one at that!

"They're tearing her down," he said in his laconic, understated way. "She'll be gone by the middle of the week." I knew instantly what he was talking about. Woodmont School had been scheduled for the wrecker ball for some time. In spite of the best efforts of neighborhood groups and the melancholy longings of thousands of us who had passed through its halls, it was finally coming down.

"I went over and watched for a while," he continued. "I'll tell you the truth. Every time another chunk of brick comes down, you can almost hear the spirits screaming."

I believed him. A lot of spirits would mourn her loss. Woodmont was more than just a building, and the brick that I already treasured was more than just a brick. It was filled with echoes from the past, brimming with reflections gathered during the passage of time.

I studied the brick, wishing it could talk. I wanted it to teach instead of me. The stories it could tell! The job was still mine, though, so I put the brick aside, thanked my friend, and began my lesson.

The text that morning was from the third and fourth chapters of John's Gospel, which narrates events at the beginning of Jesus' adult ministry.

Jesus taught the Pharisee Nicodemus while he was in Jerusalem for the Passover feast. After that, he went with his disciples into the land of Judea to baptize more followers. While he was there, he learned that the Pharisees were upset with him and might be following him, because they saw him as being in competition with John the Baptist. So after a short stay he left Judea and headed for Galilee. On the way to Galilee, he passed through a city called Sychar in Samaria. He was tired, so he paused and sat down beside a well.

What happened next is a familiar story. Jesus, a Jew, sat next to a woman, a Samaritan, and asked her for a drink. By rights they should have been enemies. They shouldn't have been talking, much less sitting together. But Jesus sat down with the Samaritan woman and chose that moment to teach us all a lesson.

You see, her nationality didn't matter. Neither did her sex, nor the nature and number of her sins. She was God's child and so was he. He had come to save everyone. All who drank of the living water would have eternal life.

There are many messages in that passage of scripture. Some of them have to do with the woman, who she was, how she reacted. Others have to do with Jesus, what he said, what he did. But the lesson I taught that morning had nothing to do with Jesus or with the woman. It was about the well.

Jacob had dug that well thousands of years earlier. The same Jacob had held on to Esau's heel at the time of their birth as if to hold him back. The same Jacob had stolen Esau's birthright as their father, Isaac, breathed his last. The same Jacob had been so frightened that he had hidden from his brother for much of his adult life. The same Jacob had died after 147 years on this earth, but before he died, had finally reconciled not only with his brother Esau, but also with his young son Joseph, whom he had long believed dead.

Jacob had left many legacies. One of them was this well, which he had dug on land he had given to Joseph.

Did Jacob know? Could he have possibly known that someday the long-awaited Messiah would sit at his well and drink of its water? Of course not. There's no way he could have known. More than likely, all he knew was that life was good and that cool, clear water was needed in order for life to continue. So he had dug a well.

I was in the middle of delivering that lesson when I realized the significance of my souvenir brick. All of a sudden it hit me. I finally understood why Woodmont was such a special place to me and to countless others.

After church was over, I rode over to the old school building. It wasn't very far away. I parked my car, got out and walked around, surveying the wreckage. The building was already half gone; the inside walls, now fully visible, still looked familiar. I was staring at the remains of what had been my eighth grade classroom.

It's a shrine, I thought. It should've been saved.

I walked around the outside of the building, and let the memories wash over me. Could I still feel it? Or was it just my imagination running wild on a Sunday afternoon?

Whatever it was, it seemed as if the years had melted away and I was walking down those halls once again.

I stood at the blackboard and struggled with a problem. I skipped down the staircase, following the warm, sweet smells into the cafeteria. I marched solemnly into the principal's office to find out what the penalty would be for some long-ago infraction. I sat again in one of the wooden desks and listened to the voices of my teachers. A million feelings came back in a flash. I was young again.

The year was 1948. Mrs. Akers was the third-grade teacher. She was a soft, gentle, lovable woman. The classroom was an old portable building that sat out back, next to the softball field. My six-year journey down those creaky, oil-soaked wooden halls had begun.

What a lucky break it was, being at Woodmont.

So much of life is chosen for us. So much just depends on chance, on how things happen to work out. I had absolutely no say in it, but I couldn't have made a better choice. We moved to Nashville, and I was deposited by fate in the midst of Ben, Ira, Gilbert, Alan, Frank, Steve, Stanley and others—bright, fun boys, sometimes crazy, always imaginative. I was thrown in with the likes of Marilyn, Nancy, Missy, Lee, Lynn, Amelia, Charlotte, Anne, and Deannie—girls I would have chosen had I been given the choice.

There are others. Naming names is dangerous because no one deserves to be left out. It was a special place, and all the people in it were special. I was at the beginning of a six-year adventure.

One boy, who shall remain nameless, holds a special place in my memory. You see, when I arrived at Woodmont in the third grade, he was the shortest boy in the class. I was in second place. At the end of that year he left, yielding the honor to me. I have never forgiven him.

Mrs. Pollard was my fourth-grade teacher. I will never forget Mrs. Pollard. She had a reputation for strictness that was matched only by reality. She demanded our best and would accept nothing less. And she always knew when she wasn't getting it, too. She was lightning quick with a ruler, but she seldom needed it. Few of us were courageous enough to act up in her class.

Although we never would have admitted it at the time, I think most of us liked the way Mrs. Pollard did things. We were young and we needed to know where the boundaries were. In her class we knew where we stood and what was expected of us. She kept us in line and pushed us beyond our limits. We were all the better for it.

When I reflect on the teachers who meant the most to me, Mrs. Pollard stands with the very best. Strong spirits need strong discipline. I know that now.

Mrs. Dixon taught the fifth grade. She was a legendary storyteller and was so popular among the students that a drawing had to be held to decide who would be in her class.

We all sat in a large room while they held the drawing. One by one the names were called. The tension mounted. My name was the last one drawn. I breathed a sigh of relief.

As it turned out, I didn't go. One of the girls was so upset and cried so hard that I gave her my place and marched off to spend the year with Mrs. Hardcastle. I was upset for about twenty-four hours. After that I never gave it another thought. The infamous Mrs. Hardcastle turned out to be a delight. It was a good year. A very good year.

Sixth grade brought on Mrs. Kershaw, another of Woodmont's legends. What a lovely woman! She gave us so much and was so patient. That same year also saw the arrival of Leonard M. Garriott. Little did I know that my whole life would be enriched by his presence.

Mr. Garriott first came to Woodmont in the spring of my sixth-grade year as a student teacher. He was a pleasant looking man with dark, wavy hair and a ruddy face. But his most fascinating and memorable physical characteristic wasn't something he had, it was something he *didn't* have. His right arm was missing. This gave him a mystique that made him special to us from day one.

What a marvelous, happy smile! What an attitude! What courage! His arm was gone, but his outlook was positive and his enthusiasm was contagious. And enthusiasm wasn't all he brought to his task that balmy spring of 1952. He also brought a full measure of discipline. We didn't see that so much during his student teaching tenure. As it happened, though, during the following summer he completed the requirements for his degree, and he came to Woodmont the next fall as a full-time seventh-grade teacher. I was assigned to his class. That's when I began to learn what he was really like.

It's also when he got to learn what I was really like.

I was full of life, or full of bull, depending on your point of view. "Free-spirited" might fit the bill. I didn't look for trouble, but I always managed to find it.

At the beginning of the school year, a new concrete walkway was being constructed from the driveway to the building. The temptation was too much. Just before the concrete hardened, I adorned a small corner of the walkway with my initials. Pleased with my handiwork, I soon repeated the process in the easily chipped paint on one of the stalls in the boys' room. Then I completed my work by deftly carving my monogram into one of the desktops.

Why did I do such silly things? I haven't the slightest idea. I hadn't yet heard that old saw about fools' names and fools' faces. As far as I was concerned, I was famous! My name was everywhere!

So was Mr. Garriott.

When he came for me, there was no place to hide.

I remember where I was standing as if it had happened yesterday. It was in the hall, next to the eighth-grade classroom door, a few feet from the entrance to the principal's office. I remember the small sheet of paper in his hand. It was pink. I could barely read it. My vision was obscured by tears. I know it had my name on it and the word "expelled." And I remember the look on Mr. Garriott's face. The twinkle was gone from his eyes. The smile was gone from his lips.

I'm glad to report that I didn't drop out and turn to a life of crime. I did, however, turn to several days of hard labor as a condition of my readmission. I removed a chunk of sidewalk and replaced it with fresh, smooth concrete. I painted the entire boys' room, at least the part I could reach. I sanded that desk until it was as smooth as a baby's bottom. Since that time I have never put my name on anything that couldn't be thrown away or quickly hidden.

After that year, for some strange reason Mr. Garriott switched to the eighth grade. Could it be that he had liked us as much as we liked him?

My eighth-grade year was nothing short of wonderful. It was like "Happy Days" on TV with younger participants, a year of fun and comradeship, a year I remember well. Short haircuts characterized the skinny boys; petticoats and angora sweaters adorned the gangly girls, who didn't look gangly at all to the skinny boys.

I remember being part of a pretty bad football team. I remember Bible study at Marilyn's every Wednesday afternoon, square dances led by Charlotte's parents, parties in the big room on the third floor at Nancy's house, and the Christmas celebration where everyone drew names. Someone else got the gift I wanted, the little silver box of Life Savers.

I remember passing out valentines and treasuring that special one from that special person. I remember cheerleaders in blue and gold, the heartbreaking loss to Harpeth Valley in the basketball tournament, Coach Alsup and his turquoise-and-black Plymouth. I remember paddlings in the principal's office, ice cream cups with movie star pictures on the lids, somebody's bicycle hanging from the flagpole. I remember the final school carnival and the last field day. I remember the ride home on my three-speed bicycle. I'd go down Estes to Auburn, turn right, then left on Woodmont, then up the hill to home.

All these thoughts and more cascaded around me like a warm, soft avalanche as I stood on the concrete walk at the edge of the last remains of Woodmont School that Sunday afternoon, the very same concrete walk I had helped build many years earlier. I shed a tear or two. Maybe more.

There's a small park there now. It's a fitting memorial, built so that future generations might find contentment and pleasure where so many of us once met the challenges of growing up. The school is gone. It is history. Its story has been written.

Or has it?

Old Jacob was smart. He knew what mattered in life. He understood the difference between things that are temporary and things that last awhile. So, he dug a well.

Mr. Garriott knew what mattered, too. So did Mrs. Pollard, and Mrs. Hardcastle, and Mrs. Kershaw—all of them and thousands of others. They dug wells. Lots of them.

How did they do it? By investing their time in things that last. They never worried about how far-reaching their influence might be, but they knew full well that what they were doing was important. They dug new wells, year after year, and let the cool water of knowledge bubble up and nourish future generations. They, and countless others like them, dedicated themselves to something far bigger than what they could see, feel, or touch. And just as Jacob could never have known that Jesus would someday pause at his well to drink, none of them could ever have guessed who might someday taste of the living water of knowledge which they imparted to countless children, in places like Woodmont.

In my memory, I can still hear the cheering voices:
We're from Woodmont, Couldn't be prouder,
Can't hear a sound, so we'll yell a little louder!

It doesn't matter that the bricks and mortar are gone. That's not what's important. It never was. The seeds are still growing, and the spirit remains. Woodmont is alive! The good work that was done in that place is being multiplied and extended even now, in ways that will never be fully known.

THE MAN IN SEAT 2-C

I don't have any fear of flying. None at all. I have a considerable fear of *not* flying, however, especially when I am in an airplane and we are up in the air.

To my great misfortune, I once read an article that stated that most air crashes happen in the first thirteen seconds after takeoff. People who fly ought to avoid articles like that. Since the day I read it, I have gritted my teeth and counted to thirteen after every takeoff. After that, I'm okay. Nervous, but okay.

This particular piece isn't about flying, though. It is about a remarkable experience I had on an airplane during a flight from Atlanta to Nashville. It's about what happened after one of those thirteen-second teeth-gritting climbs into the sky.

It was Tuesday, March 20, 1984. I was on Delta's flight 1341, sitting in seat 2-D. The plane was full. We were at one end of the runway, apparently determined to get to the other no matter what. As we picked up speed, it became increasingly apparent that this particular airplane could have used a good wheel balancing and a front-end alignment. It felt as if we were rolling on square wheels that weren't even rolling together.

Outside my window, the concrete runway flew past. I went through my customary mental exercise of wondering which would come first, lift-off or the end of the runway. By the time we reached the appropriate speed, I was bouncing up and down in my seat and the plane was clattering and clanking as if it might fly to pieces at any moment. We lifted off. The plane shuddered. I started counting. It was the longest thirteen seconds I can remember.

Once we were airborne, I flipped the latches on my briefcase, took out my Bible and a legal pad, and turned to the thirteenth chapter of the Gospel of John. I needed to prepare my lesson for the Challenge Class for the coming Sunday.

The man in seat 2-C glanced my way. He looked down at my open Bible, then back at me. He was smiling.

"Nervous, huh?" he asked.

I smiled back, but I didn't answer. I felt strangely self-conscious. Why do people always look at you funny when you take out a Bible in a public place? I switched on my reading light and went about my business. The last thing in the world I wanted was a conversation. Besides, we probably didn't have anything in common.

A few minutes later he was still looking my way, still smiling. Oh great, I thought. I'm stuck here next to a guy who's desperate for companionship. Just my luck. And I wasn't even supposed to be in seat 2-D.

I always sit on the left side of the plane, and the "D" seats are always on the right side. My travel agent knew better than to put me on the right side. "Left side, window seat, no smoking," I told her the first time I signed on with her company. "No exceptions."

"Are you superstitious?" she asked. "Is it safer on the left side? Do you know something I don't know?"

"None of the above," I replied. "I hear better in my right ear, that's all." Which is true.

Not only was I on the wrong side, but I was sitting in the wrong seat. Earlier, when I had gotten my boarding pass, I had been assigned to 5-D, not 2-D. But as luck would have it, on this particular flight 5-D was a smoking seat. When the stewardess announced that the chap in 2-D was having a nicotine fit and wanted to swap with someone, I had raised my hand so quickly that I had almost broken a finger bumping it against the overhead.

So here I was, in a seat I hadn't bought and wouldn't have asked for, looking forward to fifty-eight minutes of peace, trying to figure out how to avoid being sucked into an unwanted conversation.

I kept on working and ignored the man. It was the only thing I could think of to do. After a while he finally gave up, opened his own briefcase, and started looking at some papers. Guilt grabbed me by the heart. I began to regret my uncharacteristic unfriendliness. I couldn't concentrate on what I was doing. So I sighed, put away my pen, closed my Bible, and did the unthinkable.

I started a conversation with *him*.

Get the picture, now, because it's important to understand how many factors were working against what was about to happen.

I was in a seat I wasn't supposed to be in. I needed time to work and didn't want to talk. I have a natural aversion to conversation of any kind at sporting events and on airplanes. Especially on airplanes. In addition, I didn't particularly like the looks of this guy, so I specifically didn't want to talk to him. And I had successfully communicated my disinterest to the point that he had decided to leave me alone. Yet for some unexplainable reason, I tossed my hard-earned advantage out the window and started a conversation with him.

I'm glad I did. If I hadn't, the loss would have been mine. I would have missed a remarkable experience.

The man was a salesman from Macon, Georgia. He was going to Nashville on business, to peddle his product. He was very enthusiastic about what he was selling. He started in on me as if I were a potential customer.

He told me that what he was selling was a waste

disposal system for hospitals. That was not exactly a sure-fire conversation starter. It was his baby, though, and he talked with the enthusiasm of a proud father.

He showed me his brochure and assured me that he could save me a ton of money, if only I owned a hospital. He backed up his claim with statements from satisfied customers and with pictures of his system installed and in use at several locations.

I was quite taken aback. How could anyone be that involved, that enthusiastic, about something as uninspiring as a waste disposal system? At the risk of being offensive, I asked him that very question. In response, he began to tell me his story. Later that night, thoroughly captivated, I wrote it down, as much of it verbatim as possible.

It seems that some thirteen years earlier, he had been selling pharmaceuticals and had found himself on the loading dock at a major hospital somewhere in the South. The place was a mess. Moreover, it looked dangerous. All kinds of infectious, prurient substances sat around in open containers, festering.

"Is it always messy like this?" he had asked a worker at the hospital.

"I'm afraid so," the worker had replied. "The fellow who can figure out a system to get rid of this waste in a sanitary way can make millions," he continued.

Well, that idea had struck my seatmate right between the eyes, and over the next thirteen years he had developed and built a company that did just that. Several months prior to our flight, he had sold the company to a large conglomerate and had made the millions that the hospital worker had predicted. Under the terms of the sale, however, he would be working for the new owners for five years. After that, at the age of forty-seven, he would be ready to conquer new worlds.

I smiled pleasantly, thinking that his story was over. It

wasn't, though. There was more. From this point on, I will tell as much as I can in his words.

"It isn't fair for me to leave you with the impression that everything was easy," he said. "That's not how it was. If it hadn't been for God, I never would've made it."

Now it was he who was holding a Bible. He had slipped it out of his pocket when I wasn't looking.

"I've been born again," he said.

"Tell me about it," I responded.

I'm surprised I said that. I am usually wary of "born agains," especially when I think they are about to try to force their particular brand of religion on me without regard to my personal point of view. But something about this was different. I wanted to hear more.

His success hadn't come without a price, he told me. He had soon become obsessed with his new idea and had devoted himself wholeheartedly to its development. In his case the "price" had been the sacrifice of his personal life on the altar of achievement.

His family had been enthusiastic at first, of course. Visions of wealth do tend to obscure one's view of reality. But soon their enthusiasm had waned and their patience had worn thin. Support had turned to tolerance; tolerance had given way to bickering. Things had gone from bad to worse and then to unbearable.

He had assured them that the hard times wouldn't last forever, but he really hadn't believed it himself. In truth, he had been too committed to turn back, even though the ground felt shaky. Money had been borrowed, an investment had been made, and he had been ensnared in a trap of his own making. Thus he had suffered through long nights and weekends at work while his family ties groaned under the strain. Finally he had begun to seek solace where it was easily found.

It had been gradual at first. A social drink in the evening, then two, then several. Soon there had been a bottle in the desk drawer to make the long afternoons more bearable.

Next had come two-martini lunches and finally a bracer in the morning to help him get started. He hadn't noticed the huge fist closing around him until he was already in its grip. Even then, he had rationalized it away. He was in complete control. He could quit whenever he wanted to. No doubt about it.

"You wouldn't believe how much booze I could put down in a single day," he told me. "I would start with a juice glass full in the morning. I'd drink it straight. Before the day was done I would have killed a fifth or more, in addition to some beer or wine. It was incredible. The business was going nowhere. My wife and kids had left in tears. But all I could see was that elusive goal, and all I wanted was my friend the bottle, the friend who was going to help me get there.

"Well, it all came to a head one afternoon. I was in a small town in north Alabama. I was drunk out of my mind, driving a rental car. I was on a one-day trip. I had my working papers, a clean shirt, a change of underwear, my ever-present bottle, and nothing else.

"I pulled up to an intersection on the edge of town. The cross street I was facing was a main highway. I stopped my car. At least I thought I had stopped. Mentally, I was out of it, and the car was still moving. It kept on going out into the intersection, with me just staring blankly ahead. A semi doing sixty-five hit me broadside."

I was incredulous. "What happened?" I asked. He smiled somewhat self-consciously as he responded.

"You aren't going to believe this, but it's true. I was thrown out of that car with a terrific force. I was literally pulled out of a pair of lizard shoes—they were found in the car, right where my feet had been. My body skidded along the pavement at high speed; all of my clothes were torn off. I came to a stop about a hundred feet from the impact. All I had on was my shirt collar, my necktie, and the lapel of my suit. I must have looked awful. I was bloody, raw, and battered, but I was alive. I was conscious, but apparently no one could tell.

"The next thing I remember was two medics standing over me. They had happened on the scene by accident. I found out later that one of them was a newcomer, being trained for the job. They leaned over me and the older one said to the younger one, 'Well, you've been baptized sure enough. You've seen your first dead one.'

"I tried to scream, but nothing came out. I wanted to tell them I wasn't dead. I couldn't move. I couldn't get their attention. It was horrible.

"Soon a policeman came over to me. I watched him as he felt my pulse and listened for my heartbeat. He said I was dead, too. I was in a state of unbelievable panic. I screamed out in my mind. Dear God! Tell them I'm alive!

"They decided to take me to the hospital. I still couldn't move or make a sound. I prayed and prayed the whole time. I promised God that if he would help me get their attention, if he would help me get out of this, I would never touch another drop of alcohol again and I would be his servant forever.

"The next thing I remember is sitting on a gurney in the emergency room, talking to a doctor. The medics and the policeman were still there. They were absolutely astounded! So was the doctor. He said that when I had arrived in the emergency room, I'd had no pulse, my eyes hadn't been dilating, and he had thought I was dead, too.

"All of my wounds turned out to be superficial. For the rest of the day I was washed, scrubbed, rubbed with ointment, and patched up with bandages. Finally the decision was made to release me. It was no easy decision. No one there could believe there wasn't anything more seriously wrong with me.

"The last thing they did was to issue some hospital 'greens' to me and give me the tattered remnants of my clothes and my personal effects. I took a cab to a local shopping center and bought something to wear. Then I decided to check into a local motel and get some rest. I had no heart for trying to get back home and no real concern for notifying the scattered remnants of my family. They wouldn't care anyway, or so I thought.

"I asked the cabbie to stop by a convenience store. I bought a six-pack of cold beer, then went to the motel. I was shaking like a leaf, functioning more from rote than from will. I fumbled with the key, managed to get inside, pulled the covers down on the bed, flipped on the television, got under the covers, and popped open the first beer, giving no thought whatever to my bargain with God.

"The first image that flashed on the screen hit me like a bolt out of the blue. It was Billy Graham. He was looking right at me, pointing a finger. And I'll never forget his words. 'You have made promises to God today that you haven't kept,' he said. 'You'd better get on your knees right now, wherever you are, and ask him to forgive you.'

"Emotion poured out of me in an enormous cascade of tears and sobs. It was as if a dam had burst and every imaginable feeling was tumbling down on top of me, rolling me over and over. It was incredible.

"I have no recollection of getting on my knees, but somehow that's where I ended up, as if I had been thrown there by an angry God. I screamed out from the depths of my tortured soul. 'I need help! My God, can't you see? I can't do it alone! I don't have the strength!'

"I buried my head in my hands and leaned over, almost touching the ground with my face. Sobbing uncontrollably, I was totally helpless. I had admitted my weakness to myself and to my God for the very first time. I didn't know where to turn next. I was helpless, abandoned, lost, and alone. Where could I go for help? For strength?"

He held up his little Bible.

"I found the answer in this book," he said. "The Holy Spirit came into my body and into my life. It gave me the strength to open those beer cans, one by one, and pour that beer out. That's the hardest thing a drunk can do. I couldn't. The Holy Spirit did it for me."

I'm sure there was more, but that's all I got to hear. The landing announcement interrupted him. He said little else after that. He put away his Bible and so did I. We buckled up and sat quietly while the plane landed. I thought about asking him to go on, but I didn't. In truth, I was speechless. Later, as we gathered our things and went out into the concourse, I thanked him for telling me what he did. Then we went our separate ways.

I do not know why things happen the way they do. I have no idea why that man came into my life, opened his heart to me, then left as quickly as he had come. I cannot possibly know. But I *believe.*

"I will not leave you desolate," Jesus said in the fourteenth chapter of John. "I will pray the Father, and he will give you another Counselor, to be with you for ever, even the Spirit of truth, whom the world cannot receive, because it neither sees him nor knows him; you know him, for he dwells with you, *and will be in you.*"

The man in seat 2-C clearly believed that the promise of Jesus had been fulfilled in his life. As I heard him tell his story, I did, too.

I never saw him again. I never even heard his name mentioned. But three and a half years later, when times got tough and my own life got out of control, when things went in directions I never would have imagined, when I, too, found myself at the end of my rope, on my knees on the floor of a hotel room with nowhere else to turn and with suicide on my mind, the memory of what he told me was still in my heart. So was the Holy Spirit, thank God.

RECOLLECTIONS OF A TEE-BALL FATHER

It amazes me sometimes when I realize how many of my favorite memories involve my children.

I've been blessed with lively, lovable, likable children, and I've had the opportunity to be a part of many of the important events in their lives. For twenty-five years I have enjoyed their company. I'm very lucky.

It isn't all luck, though, and it's important for me to acknowledge that. I helped make it possible by being there for them when they wanted me there and sometimes when they didn't want me there, too. There's no substitute for presence. It's the greatest gift one can give, the greatest honor one can bestow. The memories I enjoy are, in a real sense, the dividends I am collecting on an investment in time. It's easily the best investment I ever made.

Not all of my favorite memories of my children are about the significant events in their lives. Sometimes it's the little things that stand out. I have fond recollections of small problems solved together and small fears overcome. A good example is what I call "The Great Tee-Ball Adventure."

It began on a balmy spring Sunday afternoon, many years ago, when I received a telephone call from a friend.

"I'm going to coach a Tee-Ball team," my friend said. "You think young Richard would like to play?"

"What's Tee-Ball?" I asked. I'd never heard of it.

"It's a fun game for little kids," he answered. "They get to learn all about baseball, and their dads get to learn all about patience. Sign-up is this Sunday. We'll have our first practice right after that. Come check it out. You're going to have to see it to believe it."

"Sounds great to me," I said. "I'll ask Richard and let you know right away."

I loved baseball when I was a kid, and the thought of getting to watch Richard play delighted me no end. He agreed, so the deal was sealed.

During the ensuing week, memories of my own childhood wandered freely through my conscious mind as I looked forward to the coming experience. Richard had just turned six and there were few boys his age in our neighborhood, so we hadn't had many opportunities for this sort of thing. This was just the ticket! A chance to have fun, to spend time together and to learn all about America's game!

It was also a chance for me to live my own childhood over again and to do it right, although I wasn't aware of that at the time.

We didn't have organized baseball in my neighborhood. I always wished that we did. My favorite cousin was on a Little League team in Charleston. I remember going to his games when we visited there and being intensely jealous of the uniforms, the manicured playing field, and the bleachers full of doting parents and adoring sweethearts.

We didn't have Little League, but we had baseball. We played on vacant lots. Home plate was a flat rock. The ball was almond colored and loosely stitched together. Equipment consisted of a cap and a pair of sneakers. You brought a glove if you had one; you used someone else's if you didn't. Everything else was left to one's imagination.

Fortunately, my imagination never let me down!

I was a baseball fan from the start. I always had a favorite "Nashville Vol." When we played ball, I always assumed that person's identity for the duration of the game. The player I remember best was Jack Harshman, a rifle-armed pitcher who just happened to be a power hitter as well. He was a tall, lean, handsome athlete who saved many a game for himself and for the Vols by hitting a home run just when the other team was expecting him to be an easy out, just because he was a pitcher. Crouching low over home plate, I pretended I was Jack Harshman reincarnated, ready to surprise everyone with my unexpected heroics.

Those were the days!

Of course I don't know who the other guys pretended to be, or even if they did so. Each boy's fantasy was his private property, known only to himself. In one another's eyes, and in the eyes of the world, we were just a scruffy gang of kids playing baseball in the dirt.

Anyway, after my friend's call I was excited all week! Richard, on the other hand, seemed to take it rather calmly.

I thought Sunday would never come, but it finally did. Richard and I trudged on out to Lipscomb School and put our names on the dotted lines. Thus began our season with the Brentwood Braves.

Perhaps an explanation is in order.

Tee-ball is played more or less like baseball, but the ball starts out on a "tee," which sits atop home plate, giving the batter a shot at a stationary object. It's a good thing, too, because the players are very young, and for the most part very uncoordinated.

The practices were fun to watch. In the early going, often as not the boys would miss the ball and hit the tee, sending it flying toward the unoccupied pitcher's mound. The ball, having lost its only visible means of support, would plop harmlessly to the ground. The batter, however, spurred on by the exhilaration of having hit something solid, would race toward first base, only to be called back and told to try again.

Those of us who were watching tried not to smile.

The coaches demonstrated remarkable patience. Slowly but surely, the boys began to get the hang of it. Soon it was time for the season to begin.

The games were a riot. Organized chaos! No matter how many kids showed up, they all got to play. Every one of them got a turn at bat every inning, and when it was time to hit the field, all of them scurried out to find a place to stand. Such liberality was good for morale, of course, but it also created some problems. Some of the players ended up in positions that had no official name, which sometimes made it very difficult to explain one's role on the team.

This was demonstrated to me quite vividly one sunny afternoon while I was waiting in line at the concession stand. Standing in front of me was a tiny lad, decked out in his uniform. He was obviously ready to play. With him was his grandfather, who had come along to watch.

"What position do you play?" the old man asked, clearly ignorant of the subtle nuances of the game.

"Backstop," came the confident reply.

"Oh, you mean shortstop, don't you?" the grandfather asked, unwilling to let well enough alone. "Aren't you between second and third?"

"No, I mean backstop," the future all-star insisted. "I'm between Russell and Scotty." He nonchalantly popped his fist into the pocket of his new-looking glove while his grandfather stood there, totally bewildered. I thought about explaining it to the old man, but why spoil the fun? He'd understand soon enough. His lack of knowledge was forgivable. Tee-ball was the new kid in town. This was the first season.

In Richard's league the uniforms were tattered hand-me-downs from the older boys. Richard's baseball pants draped down to his ankles. The short sleeves of his shirt reached his wrists. He looked like he was wearing a kimono. His cap obscured most of his face and much of his vision. He was a sight to behold, but he was dead serious and determined. To me, he was beautiful. The best-dressed major leaguer had never looked any better.

Richard spent that first season in the outfield, whiling away the time picking clover blossoms, daydreaming, and chasing the occasional ball that managed to trickle between the legs of the infielders. It was soon obvious that the outfield was where they put the boys they didn't want anywhere near the ball. Few of the lads could hit the ball past the infield, and there really wasn't much for the outfielders to do. By mid-season Richard had also figured out the brutal truth. Being assigned to the outfield was a one-way ticket to obscurity.

"I'm bored out there," he confessed after one of the games. "Nothing ever happens. There's nothing to do. Do you think I should say something to the coach?" I didn't think so and neither did he. He stayed with the program and did his best, deciding for himself that it was more fun to be a small part of a team than to be no part at all.

The next season, though, things were different. By virtue of his advanced age, he became an infielder. He was on a new team, too. The Pirates. It was a new start, with new teammates, a new coach, and a new uniform, hopefully one that fit a bit better. But most of all it was a shot at that ultimate achievement, a chance to get his hands on the ball. And who knows, if the stars were to come together, if the moon were to be in just the right phase, oh wonder of wonders, maybe even a pop fly would come his way! Excitement reigned! It was just perfect!

Perfect, that is, except for one thing.

A new wrinkle had been added. A new rule. To help prepare the lads for real baseball, each time a batter came up, one of the fathers from his team would pitch to him. A gentle underhand pitch, to be sure, but worlds away from the old stationary object the boys had gotten used to. To make matters worse, after three unsuccessful swings, the tee would be returned to its rightful place and the ball would be returned to the tee! Such humiliation! Imagine what it would be like to be the first boy to have the ball put back on the tee after three futile swings!

Richard was completely quiet as we drove home together after that first practice.

"What's the matter, Rich?" I asked, trying to break the ice. My gut had already answered that question, but my heart hesitated to bring it up.

"Nothing," he answered flatly, staring straight ahead. I knew better.

"You seem a little down, kid. Tell me about it."

He remained silent. So did I. We rolled along in the twilight, each feeling awkward and uncomfortable. Then, without warning, the dam burst. He blurted it out.

"This is impossible! I'm the first guy up, and I don't know how to hit the ball! This is awful! I haven't got a prayer!" He turned toward me, a pained expression on his face. "You've got to help me! We've got to practice! I don't want to make a fool of myself!"

No greater challenge was ever issued to a father!

I don't know which was the stronger, my feeling of total inadequacy or my dogged determination to help. I guess it was the latter, because we jumped right in with both feet. Every afternoon that week we marched out into the backyard, with bat, ball, and glove in hand. I taught him everything I knew. That was pitifully little, but Richard didn't seem to know or care. Somehow a father's ability always manages to rise to the level of a son's admiration.

"The most important thing," I told him, "is to look like a ballplayer. If you look like you know what you're doing, everyone will think you really do."

He listened, but I could see his skepticism. He hung in there, though, bless his heart. I was all he had.

We worked on everything! I showed him how to approach the plate, where to stand, how to crouch ever so slightly with knees flexed, how to glare at the pitcher with bat cocked menacingly, how to tap the bat on home plate and then line it up with the strike zone, as if to dare the pitcher to put one where he could reach it. I showed him all of the little things that would make a difference. Everything but how to hit the ball. Eye-hand coordination is either there or it isn't. A father cannot do anything about it, no matter how badly he wants to help.

We gave it our best, that's for sure. I must have tossed him a thousand balls. He swung at every one with the intensity and determination of the final batter for the trailing team in a world series game. It seemed to be working, too. Every now and then he'd actually hit one!

Sunday afternoon finally arrived. The whole family piled into the station wagon for the drive to the old ballpark. Everyone knew what was at stake; each of us was filled with hope and apprehension. It would take so little to make us happy. We didn't need success, only the absence of failure. Was that so much to ask?

Richard's team was in the outfield first.

I don't know what happened during that first half of the inning. I wasn't paying attention. It isn't that I didn't care. I was simply preoccupied. You see, an even *newer* wrinkle had been added. Just before the game started, the coach of the Pirates had asked me to pitch! While young Richard was getting his bat and his helmet and preparing to head for the batter's box, I was shaking like a leaf and heading for the mound.

Three pitches. That's all the chance he had. Three pitches and back to the tee. It was all the chance I had, too, unfortunately.

I tossed the first ball. It hit the ground three feet in front of the plate. Richard swung wildly. Both of us had forgotten everything we ever knew.

"Strike one," the umpire bellowed loudly. Just what we needed. A public reminder of our inadequacy.

I pulled myself together, held the ball behind me and leaned forward, as if I were waiting for a signal from the catcher. Richard just stood upright with his bat resting on his shoulder. All of his confidence was gone.

I let another one go. The ball followed a lazy arc, ending up right across the plate. Richard swung wildly a second time.

"Strike two!"

The ball had floated across waist high. I can't pitch it any better than that, I thought. I could have sworn that Richard's eyes were closed when he brought the bat around. He had swung way too late.

The father in me was going crazy! I felt an overwhelming urge to fix things, to make it okay, to come to his rescue. He seemed so small, so vulnerable. I glanced over at the stands. Barbara's face mirrored my anxiety. I turned back to Richard, served up the best pitch I could muster, and closed my eyes.

With a resounding crack the bat met the ball, sending it sailing through the air, over the infielders' heads. I raised my arms heavenward in sheer ecstasy.

Richard raced toward first. Just as he got there, the ball scooted between the left fielder's legs and on out into higher grass. Three excited outfielders converged on it, thrilled to death to finally have a ball come their way. They bumped into one another like Keystone Cops while Richard rounded the bag and headed toward second.

One of the outfielders finally fought off the other two and gained possession of the ball. By that time, Richard had stepped on second and was headed for third. The third baseman guarded the base as Richard and the ball came toward him at full speed, neck and neck.

"Slide, Richard, slide!" the coach screamed.

Good advice except for one thing. Richard hadn't learned to slide yet. Left with no alternative, he did the only thing he knew to do. He ran straight ahead at full speed. The ball went one way, the third baseman went another, and Richard headed for home under a full head of steam, pumping for all he was worth.

I was beside myself, jumping up and down with unbridled glee, shouting out incoherent words of encouragement.

The catcher retrieved the errant ball and started chasing Richard as hard as he could, but it was too late. Ten feet from home plate Richard left the ground in one final joyous leap, landing on the sacred spot with both feet. It was a home run!

I burst into tears! Everyone went wild! Everyone but Richard, that is. He took off his batting helmet, put back on his cap, dusted himself off, and strolled toward the bench, accepting his teammates' congratulations with the confident look of one who did this kind of thing regularly.

I heaved a sigh of relief and prepared to face the next batter. Richard's masculinity was saved! Come to think of it, so was mine.

We fathers don't really need all that much to make us happy, do we? Just a vicarious thrill here and there, a little triumph we can remember from time to time, magnify beyond belief as the years roll by, and embarrass our children by recounting at inopportune times. And our children? What do they need? Just a chance to give life a try, for one thing, and a dad who is present while they are trying, one who is willing to help when he's needed. And, most important of all, they need a dad whose support and love are there for the taking in equal measure, win or lose.

Of course, an occasional home run doesn't hurt, either.

MINNESOTA, NASHVILLE, 1980

Minnesota Foulk was the kind of person most people would just naturally like. That might not necessarily have been true all of his life, but by the time I met him during his forty-fourth year, the ravages of misfortune had matured and molded him into a most likable character.

Like almost everyone else who came to my office, he was there on legal business. According to our receptionist, he had asked for me by name. Since we were complete strangers, I wondered about that. He had a ready explanation. He told me that he had simply wandered into the lobby of my building and had asked the first person he saw, a man with a red beard, for the name of a good lawyer. The truth is, I didn't know anyone with a red beard back then. In any event it was a lucky break for me. Minnesota Foulk was a man worth knowing.

"Gerald Wayne Foulk is here to see you," the receptionist said when I responded to her call.

Minutes later, I was greeting a pleasant, graying, shabbily dressed fellow who looked much older than he turned out to be. We were very nearly the same age, yet he could easily have passed for my father.

He followed me back to my office, settled into a wing chair, and started telling me his story. The small room was soon filled with the comforting sound of his soft, gentle, resonant voice. His craggy face was warm and kind, and his manner of speaking belied his lack of formal education. I leaned back and listened to what he had to say.

His problem was fairly simple. He had gone to a local department store to buy a pair of pants. He had needed them badly, so he had asked if he could wait while the store's tailor hemmed them up. Waiting was one of the things Minnesota did best, since he didn't have any place to go or anyone waiting on him to get there.

He had been directed to a particular chair. While he was sitting there, a clerk who was moving furniture had dropped a heavy filing cabinet right on his foot. That would have been bad enough in normal circumstances, but for Minnesota it had been a tragedy. He had instantly lost, albeit temporarily, one-half of his only means of transportation. It was a disabling event. He was in need of a lawyer to gain some measure of restitution.

I can still see him clearly in my mind's eye.

He was a big man, with large hands and a bulky body that had obviously been muscular at one time. His hair was gray. His skin was reddish tan. His eyes were bright; they sparkled from within, and yet they were doleful at the same time.

But what defined him best was his attitude.

He had a quiet self-confidence that far exceeded what you would expect from one who was barely beyond derelict status. There wasn't a trace of arrogance. The world didn't owe him a living, and yet his hat wasn't in his hand, either. He was a man who had nothing to show for his life so far, but somehow he was hanging on to the tattered vestiges of his self-esteem. Clearly he saw in himself a spark of potential, however dim, in spite of his difficult circumstances.

I wasn't the only person who had instantly liked Minnesota. Kit Kuperstock had, too. Kit was the executive director of Project Return, a ministry to down-and-out ex-cons that operated out of the basement of Nashville's Downtown Presbyterian Church. When Minnesota had first shown up at Project Return, Kit had immediately recognized in him a sensitivity and an ability to communicate that could be put to good use.

The circumstances of his arrival at Project Return had contributed to making him special.

Minnesota had arrived at Project Return on a hot August day. He had shown up all worn out, having walked all the way from the halfway house where he was staying, a distance of nearly four miles. That would have been a heavy assignment for anyone, but for Minnesota, it was downright dangerous. He had already survived one heart attack, and he suffered from chronic angina. He was living on borrowed time. He didn't need to be plodding along Nashville's hot streets on a sultry summer afternoon.

Minnesota wasn't reticent about the trouble he'd been in. Armed robbery. Three of them, to be exact. He had been sentenced to ten years, but had been "sprung" after five because of accumulated good time. That meant that somewhere around his thirty-eighth year, this gentle, articulate, sensitive man had gone temporarily berserk and had done some very bad things.

Even before that, his life had been a series of bad decisions. He had finished high school but had gone no further. He had been a painter for many years, pursuing that trade as best he could while struggling with alcoholism. His last job before prison had been as a night-shift cook at a Waffle House. In his Project Help application, he had described his duties there as "cooking, serving food, and keeping the peace."

Minnesota knew firsthand the incredible burden of alienation and estrangement. He knew what it was like to have people blood close, but light years away. Years earlier he had married and fathered three children. His feeble attempt at parenthood had more or less ended with the completion of his biological contribution. His wife had long ago bade him farewell, taking the children with her. His children knew little about him, other than what a bum their mother thought he was. Like the pain in his physical heart, the pain in his emotional heart was his constant companion, night and day.

A wise man once said that every human being needs three things in order to sustain life emotionally—something to do, someone to love, and something to hope for. Minnesota Foulk had been in search of all three when he had made that slow, painful walk to Project Return on that thick, humid August afternoon.

He had arrived at Project Return with the clothes on his back, a few dollars in his pocket, and the engaging nickname he had acquired somewhere along the line, supposedly because of some skill at the pool table. He had absolutely nothing else. No job, no friends, no family that would claim him, and no real hope. He did have plenty of determination, though. Five years in prison gives a man time enough to think and to read a great deal. The thinking had awakened him to the error of his ways, and the reading had opened him up to the possibilities that life offered, even to one like him. He had left prison determined to reach out to his children and to fight his way back to respectability. This determination is what had carried him along the hot streets of Nashville under the burning summer sun. This same determination is what had kept him from throwing in the towel and taking the easy way out, as had so many before him in similar circumstances.

I didn't learn all of this during his initial visit, of course. As the weeks rolled by, Minnesota came to my office on a regular basis. He always popped in unannounced, but he never seemed to care how long I kept him waiting. He didn't need me much, anyway. His case was routine. All he really needed was a place to be and some people to talk to. He would sink down into one of the comfortable chairs in our reception area, content to stay there literally for hours, exchanging deep, philosophical thoughts with whoever happened to be there. Our receptionist really liked him. She made him feel comfortable and important. Our visits usually consisted of a few short moments of business followed by an hour or so of talk. I was privileged to share in his plans, his hopes, and his dreams. He wanted badly to complete his education and to go to work for a big company. He wanted an office, some place he could call his own. He wanted to wear a tie to work, and a jacket. He wanted respectability, whatever form that might eventually take.

In the summer of 1980, he took some courses at Nashville Tech. His grades were high enough for him to make the Dean's List. He received a letter from one of his professors praising his work. He carried that letter around with him forever after that. Every time he came to my office, he would take it out and read it to me. He even gave me a copy. I still have it. He was proud of that letter. It was tangible proof that his dream wasn't impossible. When a man has been on a downward slide for a long time, even a small step upward can be a real treasure.

Minnesota didn't have much to say about prison. It was obviously a sensitive subject for him. The adjustment to free life hadn't been easy. In prison, he hadn't had to worry about choices and decisions. Everything had been decided for him. When to work, when to play, when to eat, even when to turn the lights off at night. Then, after years of such treatment, he had been thrown back into the real world, a hostile environment where all the responsibilities were suddenly his again, but where few opportunities existed. He felt strong empathy for those who had been through the same experience.

Although his health and training had opened few employment doors for him, his real value was immediately recognized by Kit, and he became the receptionist for Project Return. It was a stroke of luck for him and a stroke of genius for the project.

Paul tells us, in his second letter to the Christians at Corinth, that we are to be ambassadors for Christ wherever we are. The folks at Project Return were doing just that. It was Christ's embassy in the land of the downtrodden, a land foreign to most of us. Seated at the front desk, Minnesota Foulk was the first taste of new wine for many who came through that door.

Interesting, isn't it, the ones Christ chooses to use? Who among us would have entrusted first-line responsibility to the likes of Minnesota Foulk? Yet the mantle of Christ had been draped around the shoulders of this sad-eyed man, and it fit beautifully.

Minnesota took to his new responsibility, and to the trust that it implied, with great enthusiasm. When timid souls pushed open the old wooden door, Minnesota invited them in, gave them coffee, and counseled with them in his own elementary way. His style wasn't complicated. He made them think he cared, because he really did. He offered warmth and attention to those who hadn't felt such compassion in a long time. He would empathize, not criticize. His roughhewn exterior gave people confidence; his compassionate heart gave them hope. His presence was a morale boost for all concerned. He was a ray of sunshine at a time when this underfunded project needed it badly.

Minnesota rented a room at a hotel for transients near the church. As summer yielded to fall, he started riding a bus to his job. But rain or shine, he came every day. He was filling a need and filling it well.

Slowly but surely, he began to feel more of his self-worth returning. He scrounged around for used paperback books to fill his meager shelf, and spent his evenings immersed in Faulkner, Hemingway, and Steinbeck. Very tentatively, he began to reach out beyond the project offices, to explore the old church, and to consider the possibility that he, too, might know the faith that his friends at the church demonstrated.

In the church's beautiful domed chapel, Minnesota reflected on his life and its purpose.

He attended the Reverend Pat McGeachy's Wednesday Worship and Meal, soon becoming a regular there. He reveled in Pat's unique psalm-singing ministry. There was an instant bonding between the two men. Pat's enthusiasm and plainspoken faith touched Minnesota deeply, and he began to open up. The two of them counseled and prayed together, each cherishing the friendship and strengthening the faith of the other.

As Minnesota began to find acceptance and to feel good about himself again, he began to yearn to reestablish his relationship with his children. Finally, he took pen in hand.

Letters began to flow back and forth, tracing invisible lines across the gap like so many fragile fibers, which, though weak individually, may someday weave themselves into strong cords. There was even a visit. Although there were no immediate miracles, the foundation of a relationship was being built.

Minnesota was keenly aware of his own tenuous hold on life. While he expressed no fear of death, he did express a fear of dying without reconciliation. The time had come, he would say, to get on with the job of living and to get along with his children. Yet he understood how difficult it must be for them. He knew firsthand how hard it was to suddenly trust someone who had let you down all of your life.

How wonderful it would have been if there had been a miraculous conversion in the life of Minnesota Foulk. What a heartwarming moment it would have been when he finally embraced his children, and they him. What a marvelous story it would have made, a family suddenly casting down the barriers that had built up during the years; people reaching out to one another in an emotionally cleansing outpouring of newfound love. But this is real life. His story had no such fairy-tale ending.

On an October day in 1981, Minnesota Foulk's courageous heart simply stopped beating while he slept. He was on his way to recovery, but he wasn't there. He was on his way to reconciliation, but it hadn't happened yet. Like the rest of us, he was a man on a journey, a sinner on his way home. In real life, progress comes in inches, not in miles. It's the direction we're going in that matters, not how fast we go.

Two of Minnesota's children came to the memorial service Pat held at the church. It was an eye-opener for them. They learned things about their father that they hadn't known, how he had reached out to other ex-cons and helped them make meaningful changes in their lives, how he had learned about the great southern writers and had read some of their works, how he had put his own life back on the right road, how he had put some of his own thoughts on paper in an effort to communicate in his own way. It was a genuine catharsis. For the very first time, they had something positive to cling to. At long last, they knew their father as a man who was working hard to become what God had intended him to be all along.

I'm told that after the service, the children went to his room to gather his belongings. They sorted and divided his books and papers, handling them like the treasures they were, outward signs of a man who loved God, in whose life the miracle of reconciliation was taking place, slowly but surely.

The miracle of reconciliation has been around a long time.

The latter chapters of the book of Genesis deal with the tragic alienation of the brothers Jacob and Esau.

With his mother's help, Jacob managed to steal Esau's birthright by deceiving their dying father, Isaac. Jacob got more than he'd bargained for, however. He got his father's blessing, but was separated from much of his family. He and his descendants wandered about for years, longing for relief.

Finally, he'd had enough pain. He summoned his courage and sent a message to his estranged brother, suggesting a reunion. This simple act began the process that would eventually bring them back together after all those years.

Jacob wasn't comfortable with his decision, though. He had extended the invitation, to be sure, but in truth he was afraid. When the news of his brother's pending arrival finally came, Jacob was so afraid that he divided his people and his belongings into two camps, so that if Esau and his army were coming in anger, only half of the house of Jacob would be destroyed and the other half would survive. But Esau didn't come in anger. The miracle of reconciliation had warmed his heart.

God's love was at work thousands of years ago in the lives of Jacob and Esau. In the spring of his last year on earth, when Minnesota Foulk wrote the first letter to one of his children, God's love was still at work, still healing wounds, still repairing the ties that are supposed to bind, but so often don't. God is there when we need him. We separate. God reconciles, when he is asked to do so. God waits patiently for us to cry out. Our cries are always heard; God's help is always available.

As Minnesota Foulk's life demonstrates, it's never too late to begin again.

MIRROR, MIRROR, ON THE WALL

In the sixth chapter of Matthew, Jesus tells us not to be anxious about our lives, about what we eat and drink, about what we wear. He is pretty specific about it, too. Anxiety isn't going to add a second to your life, he tells us. Not one second. Do you need proof? Just look at the lilies of the field. Look at the birds of the air. Doesn't God love you more than he loves them?

Jesus even has a name for those of us who constantly worry about the things of this world in spite of the promise of God. He calls us "ye of little faith." I have to use the pronoun "us," because I am definitely in the group he was talking about. More often than I care to admit it, I am one of those of "little faith."

I am a chronic worrier. For me, nothing is ever "enough." I am constantly anxious about what will happen when "enough" is gone. I can read Jesus' words and understand them, but I can't stop worrying. I'm getting better about it, but I can't seem to stop.

My anxiety is an affront to God. I know that. It delivers an offensive message. It says "I don't believe what your son Jesus said. I don't believe you will take care of me." It denies the existence of his miraculous power. Yet anxiety all too often has had me in its grip.

Consider the lilies of the field. Seek first the kingdom of

God and his righteousness. I need to hear that from time to time. Those words help me keep my head on straight, which is sometimes hard for me to do. There are times when the glamour and glitter of this world are almost overwhelming.

This is about one of those times.

A few years ago, Barbara and I gathered up all three children, stuffed as much of our "stuff" as we could fit into our suitcases, and headed west for a vacation.

Think about it. Imagine the beauty of the Great Plains, the majesty of the snow-capped Rocky Mountains, the grandeur of the desert Southwest, and the breathtaking panorama of the Grand Canyon. Picture the Black Hills of South Dakota with the faces of Mount Rushmore staring down at you. Picture the craggy spires of the Badlands. Picture endless stretches of the Painted Desert with majestic mountains in the background.

The image raises goosebumps.

Think about the blue waves of the Pacific lapping against rocky shores. Think about water so clear you can see the sandy bottom. Think for a moment about huge redwood trees—so large that our entire family of five could stand with hands joined and arms outstretched and still not reach around them. Think about camping out under a western sky, breathing air so clean you can hardly tell it's there, looking up at stars sparkling like brilliant jewels set in a dark velvet canopy.

Takes your breath away, doesn't it?

Well, we missed all of that. We flew over some of it on our way to Hollywood, but we didn't see it. But don't pity us. We were too excited about going to Hollywood to care about what we were missing.

At the time, all three of our children were dabbling on the fringes of show business and harboring dreams of stardom, and I must confess that such thoughts had passed through my mind on occasion, too. I had visions of becoming a great screenwriter back then. I was going to be the toast of the coast. Perhaps *this trip* would make the difference.

By the time the airplane landed, our excitement had reached a fevered pitch. We gathered our belongings, piled into a rental car, and hit the San Diego freeway, headed north.

There it was, everything we had dreamed of. Five lanes of bumper-to-bumper traffic. The unbelievable canopy of smog, so thick you think it might be solid to the touch. Palm trees swaying in the breeze. The Slauson cutoff. Wilshire Boulevard and Rodeo Drive. Sunset Boulevard. The Capitol Records building in the distance. The original Frederick's of Hollywood. Hollywood and Vine.

There's as much phoniness as there is smog in Hollywood. You don't have to be there very long to begin to wonder if there is anything left in this world that is real.

The impression begins at the movie studio. That's where we were, bright and early the next morning, the first day of our West Coast extravaganza.

At Universal Studios, we were treated to demonstrations of all kinds of special effects, including a fascinating process called matte painting, by which the actors on a studio back lot can be magically integrated into incredibly realistic paintings depicting anything from far-off lands to outer space, so that when the film is shown on the screen, the actors seem to be in places far from where the film was made, sometimes in places that don't even exist.

We watched young people grow old in minutes through the magic of makeup. We saw models of buildings that looked full-sized and real when shown on the screen, and miniature spaceships suspended in midair by wires that no longer seemed to exist once the special effects people were through punching the buttons on their computers. And we saw the back lots, those fascinating villages where all the buildings are false fronts and nothing is what it seems to be.

In one of these back lots, we took a ride through the city

square where Professor Harold Hill, the Music Man himself, once led the River City Marching Band. We stood in front of the Bates Motel and gazed upward at the old house where Norman Bates kept the remains of his mother in *Psycho*. We stopped in front of the house that Beaver Cleaver called home, down the street from the fraternity house in *Animal House*, just around the corner from the handsome dwelling of Marcus Welby, M.D.

We lingered for a moment in front of the town clock that had ticked away the seconds, almost keeping Michael J. Fox from going "back to the future." When we moved on to make way for the next group, we looked back at where we had been, only to find that there was nothing there. We had been riding along in front of false fronts surrounding a well-crafted illusion. It was all appearance and no substance. In a way it was sad.

Minutes later, on a ninety-degree California day, our tram barely avoided a flash flood. We skirted the edges of a major rainstorm, plowed our way through a blizzard, cut through a steamy jungle, and ended up in a desert. We were almost hit by a runaway train, nearly fell from a collapsed bridge, barely missed being eaten alive by a shark, foiled a kidnapping attempt by creatures from outer space, and rode across the Red Sea while the waters parted at the command of a teenaged Moses leading a group of tourists.

It was incredibly realistic, but incredibly unreal.

Halfway through the first day I was already beginning to wonder if the tall buildings on Wilshire Boulevard were really there, or if they were simply part of the illusion.

That afternoon, we walked down Hollywood Boulevard. The people we saw there didn't look any more "real" than the fantasy images we had seen at Universal.

There were dozens of young men and women (it was hard to tell one from the other) with unbelievably bizarre hairdos. Some had enormous fans of gelatinous-looking hair jutting from the center of their heads. Others had bright yellow hair sticking out in all directions like long, golden spikes. Still others had multicolored ponytails or shoulder length braids. Many wore clothes made of dark leather with heavy metal studs and spikes sticking out all over them, making them look like medieval executioners with clown masks. Others looked like creatures from outer space in their bright colored outfits with exaggerated shoulders and cuffs. They were everywhere, walking the streets in groups. It was as if they were part of some weird contest in which the most outrageous would be the winner.

The thing that struck me most was the enormous amount of time it must have taken them to make themselves look like that, to say nothing of the money.

It was sad. Very sad. It broke my heart to see God's creatures so distorted and abused. It made a mockery of the beauty of his handiwork. If some misguided monster were to desecrate the lilies of the field by spraying them all with dayglow paint, the result would not be any more tragic. And the saddest part of all was the realization that the reason these people had done this to themselves was so they could belong, be accepted, and feel good about themselves.

As the California sun neared the end of its downward slide, there was just enough time for us to drive through Beverly Hills and see some of the beautiful people.

They, too, all looked alike.

Open-collar shirts and gold chains were commonplace. Dark glasses were propped up on hundreds of heads, or hanging jauntily from the collars of hundreds of sweaters. Puccis and Guccis walked side by side, several deep on every sidewalk. Designer labels were everywhere. Tan skin was equally ubiquitous, and there wasn't a wrinkle to be seen. And all of these impeccably dressed men and women zipped from place to place in the most incredible collection of automobiles I had ever seen. Mercedes, Jaguars, and Porsches were too numerous to care about.

Ferraris, Lamborghinis, and DeLoreans were idling at every red light. Corniche convertibles came along one after another.

It was clear that the perfect people on Rodeo Drive were no different from the spiked-hair unisexes on Hollywood Boulevard. They, too, were willing to spend whatever it took to feel good about themselves.

That evening, worn-out and mind-boggled, we staggered back to our quaint little hotel on Wilshire Boulevard. After everyone else had gone to bed, I spent some time sitting alone, trying to unwind from our first day in this alien world. I glanced through the pages of a weekly newspaper that had been available in the lobby of our hotel. An advertisement caught my eye. I couldn't believe it.

How appropriate, I thought. Where else would I find something like this?

In the advertisement, a slender, picture-perfect young woman was standing by an open door. The room she was in had an intimate feel. Her expression, and the way she leaned against the doorframe, suggested that someone she cared about had just left.

She was wearing an elegant negligee. Her blonde hair was brushed to a sheen. Her skin had a radiant glow. With gently curved fingers she was holding a flower that some admirer had given her, perhaps the person who had just left. He (an assumption on my part) had undoubtedly given it to her because of her beauty. She looked happy and satisfied. The ad told us why she looked that way. "Life looks better when *you* do," it read.

What were they selling? Was it vitamins? Exercise equipment? Aerobic dance tapes? No. The ad was for a service called "You're Becoming," which was being offered by the Beverly Hills Center for Special Surgery. Apparently the Center was offering for sale a veritable smorgasbord of perfect body parts.

According to the ad, for a modest fee I could correct

God's mistakes and undo the mess he made when he created me. They would straighten my nose, lift my face, trim my brows, reshape my chin, or remove unwanted fat, and they would be willing to do it in the evening or on Saturday if I couldn't come in the daytime. Was I short on cash? No problem. They offered easy terms, one-day service, financing on the spot.

The ad didn't say anything about a drive-in window, but it wouldn't have surprised me.

I couldn't help thinking that the whole look-at-me syndrome was reminiscent of the wicked queen in *Snow White*. Remember her? She was the one who was hung up about having to look better than anyone else. Actually, in the Disney version she wasn't bad looking at all. Rather attractive, really, even though her meanness detracted somewhat from her appearance.

Every morning she got up, put on her makeup, and dressed to the nines. Every morning she looked like a million bucks. She was the Queen; she had access to the best her kingdom had to offer—the best clothes, the best hairdressers, the best makeup artists, the best jewelry, everything. But every morning, before she could feel good about herself, she had to get a second opinion.

"Mirror, mirror, on the wall, who is the fairest of them all?" she would ask. And the answer was never the one she wanted.

Poor, poor Queen. She couldn't just enjoy the beauty she had been given. She was too insecure, too dissatisfied with herself. When she didn't get the right answer she would work even harder, even to the point of eliminating whomever the mirror preferred that particular day.

I wonder how many of the people I had seen that day would have loved to have such a mirror.

None of this is limited to California. It's everywhere. It's you and me and everyone we know. It's the direction our world is going in, as fast as it can get there.

Think about how much time, energy, effort, and money

we spend so we can feel good about ourselves and be satisfied with the image we put forth for the rest of the world. We all want desperately to be liked, maybe even to be loved. We long for acceptance, for the feeling called "okay." We work at it, day and night. We build our sets, our false fronts, and then we hide behind them until pretty soon the unreal front we have created becomes our reality. Then we start comparing. We measure ourselves against false standards that can *never* be met, and when we fail to measure up, we lose confidence. So we try harder. Each effort brings new failure and another loss of confidence. A vicious cycle starts, and soon we are trapped. Soon we are nothing but an image, held together by an occasional compliment, desperately searching for the affirmation that can only come from within.

I put the newspaper down in disgust and picked up a book. It was a long time later before I finally got to sleep. The next morning we were ready to go again.

The days flew by. There was a lot to see, and we tried our best to see it all. The pace wore us all out. Even the children got tired. On the last morning, they slept in while Barbara and I walked over to Westwood Village to have breakfast at a delightful French cafe with umbrellas and tables out front. The weather was beautiful, so we sat outside and ordered. It was very pleasant, almost idyllic, until the sirens raced by. Soon it was quiet again.

On the way back, we took the long way. We strolled up Westwood Boulevard to Wilshire, crossed Wilshire, which was no easy task, then drifted eastward along Wilshire, toward our hotel. The morning air was cool, crisp, and pleasant. The traffic was heavy. We weren't in a hurry. As we strolled along in front of the sparkling clean skyscrapers, we chatted aimlessly about our departure schedule and reminisced about the week we had enjoyed.

Barbara noticed it first, then she pointed it out to me. So *that's* what the sirens had been about.

Several policemen were standing around the entrance to

a courtyard in front of one of the tall buildings. They were talking and seemed very casual; one of them was even smiling. No one seemed particularly excited or distressed, even though the whole courtyard was blocked off by bright yellow tape inscribed "Police Line. Do Not Cross."

Drawn by curiosity, I left Barbara and walked up to the tape that blocked the stairs leading into the courtyard. There, in the open courtyard, was the unmistakable form of a body, covered by a sheet. As it turned out, at about the time Barbara and I had been served our breakfast, some embittered, depressed soul had jumped from the top of that antiseptic building and had plunged to his death on the glistening marble pavement, very near a man-made fountain, a few steps from a stone sculpture of some kind. While Barbara and I had been talking pleasantly and enjoying each other's company, this nameless form had come face to face with himself and had been unable to find anything worthwhile in what he saw.

I stood there, stunned, staring at the lifeless body. Then I said a little prayer for this stranger whom we had seen only in death.

As we walked away, I was overwhelmed by the contradiction of it all, the specter of death in this place, in the midst of all of this artificial beauty. I wasn't shocked, though. In a world that is so preoccupied with false appearances, false hopes, and false values, it isn't surprising when someone decides that the quest is too much.

It was too late for him, whoever he was, but it isn't too late for the rest of us. There is hope, and there is help. That's what the Good News is all about. Life is not a contest. The winner isn't the one who has the most stuff or looks the best. Life is a journey. The winner is the one who knows what is important, who finds peace within himself, and who enjoys the journey one day at a time.

In truth, we don't have to struggle with the impossible task of finding lasting satisfaction in the trappings of life.

We don't have to surrender to temptation, or lose ourselves among the unsavory, or escape with chemicals. We don't have to kill ourselves. The reality of life is this: there isn't anything wrong with us just the way we are.

God created each of us to be something special. He created us in his image and made us just a little less than the angels themselves. We are more than the lilies of the field and the birds of the air. We are the best of God's handiwork. We are worthy. We are okay. We don't have to spend our lives chasing an impossible dream or measuring ourselves against an impossible ideal. We can love ourselves just like we are, because we are worthy of love.

God made us, and God don't make no junk.

TO LINDY, WITH LOVE

In 1985, I was the featured speaker at the Harpeth Hall School Father-Daughter Banquet. To this day, that remains one of my happiest experiences.

Three hundred young women were present that evening, along with an equal number of fathers, grandfathers, uncles, or devoted friends. Lindy, my second daughter, was seated next to me at the head table. It was the spring of her senior year, and except for her graduation, this was to be our last special event at her all-girl school. I directed my remarks to everyone there, but Lindy was the only person on my mind the whole time.

Lindy was, and is, a very special young woman. Being next to her at the head table and being able to say the things I said that evening brought me as much pleasure as anything I have ever done in my life. I can't compile a collection without trying to recapture that experience.

This is for Lindy, for all the fathers and daughters who were there that evening, and for *all* fathers and daughters who love each other in the special way that only they can know. Here it is, just as it was delivered on that magic evening.

I was sitting in my easy chair watching television, minding my own business, when the telephone rang. I didn't answer it, of course; it's never for me anyway. The phone hasn't been for me in years. But this time it was! Lindy let me know about the call, but urged me to hurry up, since she had someone on the other line.

"This is Warren," the familiar voice announced. Warren was a close friend and was president of the Fathers' Club. "I want to know if you'll be the speaker at this year's father-daughter banquet. How about it?"

I was taken aback. I wanted to know more. Had he heard one of my marvelous speeches? Had my outstanding reputation reached his ears? I was curious.

"Why me?" I asked.

"Well, we talked about it at the Fathers' Club and decided that what we wanted was no speaker at all. You were the closest thing to no speaker at all we could think of."

He's right, I guess. I'm an ordinary speaker. But you are clearly no ordinary audience. You are a very diverse group. Many talents are represented here, as are varying degrees of intelligence and ambition. No two of you are alike, yet you share several common characteristics. You are all bright, hardworking, and ambitious.

Wherever I might be, whenever I see a young lady wearing Dress Campbell, the familiar Harpeth Hall tartan, I immediately feel a kinship. Right away, I know she's someone special. I guess I'll always feel that way.

You will note, young ladies, that I have addressed *you* as the audience. By doing so, I left some people out. Also present tonight are your fathers, your grandfathers, your uncles, and your dear friends: men who love you very much. But I'm not going to speak to them. I'm going to speak *for* them. I love Lindy, and I have fashioned these remarks with her in mind. The men who are sitting with you love you just as much. In deciding what to say, I have also thought about what they would say to you if they had their chance. So, I speak for them. While I speak, I hope you will be aware of the love they feel for you tonight and will know how proud they are of you.

I am a father. It should come as no surprise to you that a father would make a speech. That, after all, is one of the things fathers do best.

How many times has your own father made a speech about your grades, your clothes, your dating habits, your table manners, or any one of those subjects that make the hair stand up on the back of your neck? You've probably thought, or even said out loud, something like this:

"Oh Daaaddy, not again!"

Note the drawn out pronunciation of "daaaddy." When it's said that way, the rest of the sentence isn't necessary. We fathers know what's coming next. We know, for example, that mother nature has given you certain natural defenses against the fatherly speech. Even though you may have come to take them for granted, they kick in place automatically, as soon as you realize what's coming.

The realization comes first. "Hey, this clown's about to make another speech," you say to yourself. Then your expression turns to disinterest and freezes into place. Your eyes glaze over. Your shoulders slump as if the burden is too much to bear. Your mind shifts into neutral, then wanders off. You steel yourself to endure what is coming.

If by chance your father happens to ask you a question during his "speech," no problem! You know all of this by heart anyway, and your answer is always the same.

"Yes, Daddy. I understand."

Well, I don't want to trigger your defenses. I want you to stay with me and listen. So, I'm being up front about it. A speech is on its way. Don't tune out.

Not only is a speech on its way, but I'm also going to exercise my prerogative to do something else that may trigger your defenses. I'm going to give you some advice.

Before you start moaning and groaning, let me assure you that advice-giving is more than just a fatherly responsibility. It is a fatherly right.

You want proof? Look in the dictionary. Under "father," you will find three definitions: (1) an ordained priest, (2) a male parent who has nothing to do during the birth process, but spends the rest of his life claiming full credit for the child, and (3) an all-wise male parent who has every right to give his children advice. So you see, my advice-giving role is legitimate. It is simply part of being a father.

I'll let you in on a secret. Perhaps you have heard about the classes that the Red Cross puts on for expectant parents. Well, they don't keep the men and women together in those classes. While the women are in one room learning to powder bottoms, the men are in another room, being taught how to make fatherly speeches. They are taught such things as the art of confrontation, the importance of timing, the skill of finger pointing, how to assume the "I mean it this time" expression, and how to block a bedroom door without being obvious. These are drilled into them for hours.

If fathers pass the speechmaking class, they become eligible for advanced courses in such topics as advice-giving, sheepish grins, how to look like you know what's going on when you don't, and the all-time favorite, how and when to "ground" your child for the weekend.

Now you know why your father was never willing to change your diapers, but was always willing to run your life.

Don't be fooled, though. Being a father is no bed of roses, at least not in the early years. Fathers really do go to those baby-care classes. We try our best to learn what to do, but when the baby comes, we are useless. Furthermore, we are ignored. Sure, we still have our basic skills, such as speechmaking and advice-giving, but when our daughters are little babies, we can't do anything with them. You fathers know what I'm talking about. It's a waste of time to stand over a crib, point to a soiled diaper and say, "That does it, young lady! You're grounded!" All you get in return is a gurgle, or maybe a burp. And it's equally frustrating to give advice to an infant. "It's a jungle out there," you say as you hold her on your lap and look into her sparkling eyes. Somehow you get the feeling that she's not taking you seriously, but you go ahead and give the advice anyway, because you know that someday soon she'll be rolling her eyes and saying "Oh, daaaddy!"

We survive, though, and so do our daughters. After a while that magic time comes when they are old enough to listen, to understand, and perhaps even to care. That's when we finally become useful, mistakes and all. Fortunately for all of us, a father's mistakes are rarely fatal. Mine weren't, and by now I have given enough advice and made enough speeches to have a pretty good idea of what is important and what is not. So bear with me, won't you? This may not be great advice, but it will be pretty good. I hope someday you'll look back on this experience and be glad that you heard it.

Piece of advice number one. Be female.

That may seem a bit silly at first. After all, you *are* female. But it really isn't silly at all. One of the most important decisions you will ever make is the decision to be truly female, in the best sense of that word.

More years ago than I care to remember, I walked through the front door at Vanderbilt Law School to begin my professional education. There were three women in my class of one hundred and twenty-five students. Two decades later, almost half of the incoming students were female. By now the percentage is even higher. I am told that similar increases have been experienced in medicine, engineering, business, and all the professions. Women are taking their rightful places in the mainstream of America's professional society, and many of you will do the same.

I feel fortunate to have lived at a time when I could witness, firsthand, the women's revolution. During that time, I have observed that women in the professional ranks seem to be falling into two distinct categories.

One category is made up of women who believe that in order to compete with men, they have to be "like" men. They have to dress like them, act like them, congregate where they gather, beat them at their own games. In the process, in their effort to become acceptable to the males around them, some of these women have begun to "put down" all things traditionally female—feminine charm, feminine dress, even motherhood and homemaking. These women are gaining much, but they are giving up something they didn't have to lose in order to get where they want to go.

The other category is made up of women who still recognize the essential value of their femininity. These women take the gifts they were given at birth and use them to the fullest. They live their lives as talented, capable, intelligent, and charming women, walking tall in all arenas of life, from the traditional role of motherhood to the farthest frontiers of science, business, and the professions. These women are a pleasure to know and a challenge to compete against. They, too, are getting what they want, but not at the expense of other women and certainly not at the expense of their own essential femininity.

That second group represents what I mean when I advise you to be female. Rejoice in who and what you are. Use the assets you have been given to make a better world for yourself, wherever you choose to make it. But at the same time, respect the right of men, and the right of other women as well, to make the choices that are right for them.

Piece of advice number two. You've got to have style.

This advice isn't original to me. It was first given to me by Mrs. Sims, my Latin teacher, when I was a freshman in high school. It was given regularly, always with a great deal of flair and with a lot of enthusiasm. She would stand in front of the classroom day after day, look down on our motley crew of skinny freshmen, and exhort us, with great emphasis, to be unique. "You've gotta have style." Clearly she could see some potential that wasn't evident to the naked eye.

I didn't know what she meant back then, but I could tell she was serious and her words stayed with me. Years later, I began to understand.

A lot of people in this world spend a lot of time imitating one another. They try their best to dress like one another, talk like one another, drive the right cars, live in the right neighborhoods, and belong to the right clubs. They may be safe but they are lost in the crowd, and bored.

On the other hand, even in this cookie-cutter world where sameness is elevated to an art form, some people still manage to be special. Some people are true to their own feelings, work toward using their talents, and eventually realize their potential. Some people take a risk. They live on the cutting edge of life, and they reap the rewards that go with it. These are the people who are excited about life. They are the ones who stand out in the crowd. They are the ones who have style.

Don't you realize how special you are? How unique? You are one of a kind! Believe it, and have the courage to show it! Have a little style. Use your special talents. Take chances. Let your natural craziness come through. Have a little fun while you are here on earth.

Now for piece of advice number three. This is something another woman said many years ago, only in this case I didn't know her, and she didn't say it to me.

Lillian Hellman was a playwright whose career flourished in the thirties and forties. Some of her plays, such as *The Children's Hour, The Little Foxes,* and *Toys in the Attic,* have become classics. She was a wonderfully talented woman. She had a gift and she used it well.

In the early fifties, she ran afoul of Senator Joseph McCarthy in his relentless search for people in the entertainment industry who allegedly sympathized with Communists. As a result of her refusal to testify before the McCarthy Committee, Lillian Hellman was blacklisted and was unable to get work in Hollywood for many years.

Was she right or was she wrong? I don't know. That isn't relevant here. Rightly or wrongly, she stood for something. She stood firmly on her principles, even though it cost her a promising career.

A few years ago, *Time* magazine reported her death and printed her picture. Under that picture was a single quote. It wasn't from any of her literary works, as fine as they were. It was from a letter that she wrote to the McCarthy Committee right after that committee had unsuccessfully sought to have her testify. It is that quote from Lillian Hellman's letter that inspired my third piece of advice.

"I cannot and will not cut my conscience to fit this year's fashions."

When I first read that, I was stunned by the simple wisdom of her words. There are some things in life that simply do not change with the fashion of the year. One of those things is truth. Another is honesty. Still others are integrity and self-respect. These things are eternal. They never change. They are always appropriate.

During your life you will have many opportunities to compromise. You'll be able to stretch the truth or avoid it altogether, and nobody else will know. The easy way will always be available to you. You'll have your chance to grab the pleasures of the moment at the risk of honor, self-respect, and personal integrity. When these opportunities come, when you feel alone in the crowd, when you are feeling pressure from others and have nothing going for you except for your own sense of right and wrong and your dogged determination to do the right thing, remember the words of Lillian Hellman, and stay on your own course.

Don't ever cut your conscience to fit somebody else's fashion.

Well, I guess that's all the advice I have.

Now, I want to let you in on a secret. I had a plan when Lindy was born. It was a plan for fatherhood. I was going to be the best father ever. I was going to be available to her, a counselor, a guide through troubled pathways, a fan who would cheer her on in times of triumph, a friend who would be there in times of tribulation. I expect that my plan was not unlike that of every father who ever held a tiny, red-faced daughter in his arms.

Plans don't always work out like we want them to, though. Mine didn't. Not all of them, anyway. Pressures built up. Life took strange and cruel turns. Good ideas were put off until tomorrow; good intentions seldom resulted in action. All the while, the years flew by.

Let me tell you what it's like, young ladies.

For a while, a daughter is a buddy. She's a companion. A pal. Then one day the door to her room is closed, and fathers don't understand what is happening. Soon they start opening the front door to the insistent knocking of skinny young boys who have come to claim what is theirs. After a while, the boys are bigger and not quite as skinny. Eventually, fathers find themselves at the point where they are no longer the most important men in their daughters' lives. They find themselves facing a melancholy fact of life: they will never be number one again. They are proud of their daughters' successes, to be sure. But their hearts cry out for the little girls they once knew, the ones who were once there, but so quickly gone.

Young ladies, when you go home tonight, you will carry with you the rose you were given when you arrived. You will probably put it in water and display it in a prominent place for a few days. After a while it will lose its beauty, and you will want to put it away. Well, I have a suggestion.

Press it between the pages of a book, or tuck it away in the pages of your memory. Keep it where you know it will be when you come looking for it again. Then someday, years from now, when you are a little down, when life's burdens seem more than you can bear, come back to that rose. Pick it up. Hold it in your hands.

When you do that, remember what we have talked about. Remember to rejoice in your femininity and make the most of it. Remember to have style, to be special, just like each of these roses is special. Remember to stand your ground and not cut your conscience to fit anybody else's fashion.

But if by chance you have long ago forgotten all of that and can remember just one thing, let it be this: that on the night you received that rose, you were with someone who loved you very, very much.

THE DAILY DIARY
OF THE AMERICAN DREAM

I don't usually watch commercials. I keep the "mute" button handy, and I use it. But this one caught my eye.

A voice, deep and resonant, was extolling the virtues of upward mobility. Handsome young men and women were marching about efficiently, full of energy and confidence, each clearly headed for "success," and all for the same reason. They read the right newspaper.

"The *Wall Street Journal* is the daily diary of the American dream," the announcer told me. Then the music faded and the football game came back on.

Why would the *Journal* need to be advertising? I wondered that to myself. It is, after all, an American institution. Its articles are constantly being discussed. It is seen in all the right waiting rooms, in all the right offices. In the best hotels it is delivered to your room. In the best conference rooms it is clearly visible on a side table. It is the accepted symbol of awareness, business acumen, and upward mobility. So why does it need to advertise?

Actually, in my heart of hearts, I have always wanted to be a *Wall Street Journal* kind of guy. I have always wanted to be one of those men who goes down to a stockbroker's office every afternoon, sits in an overstuffed leather chair with nailhead trim on the arms, smokes a cigar, watches (and perhaps even understands) the overhead tape that shows all of the current stock market transactions, reads the *Wall Street Journal*, and really cares about what it says. I can just see myself sitting there, making money without lifting a finger, smiling benignly and nodding at the other men when the *Journal* says something solid and conservative.

Thus far it hasn't happened.

Don't pity me, however. My life hasn't been entirely impoverished. I actually owned a copy of the *Journal* once.

It happened in my first year in law school, right after I had figured out for the first time that the world was divided into two groups: the elite, and the rest of us. The elite, it seemed, always carried a copy of the *Journal*. It was always folded and always visible, but never obvious. It was understated and omnipresent. A tasteful status symbol.

Day after day I observed fellow students carrying their *Journals*. Day after day I was impressed. Day after day the *Journal* looked the same. Then it dawned on me. It was impossible to tell one day's *Journal* from another, unless you got very close to it.

A bright light flashed on in my brain. It really was possible for a fellow with a *Mad Magazine* mentality to have a *Wall Street Journal* reputation on a *Reader's Digest* budget. I didn't have to wallow in mediocrity all of my life. I, too, could be a mover and shaker. I bought a *Wall Street Journal* of my own. What a proud moment!

I folded my *Journal* just so, with the masthead showing, and placed it in my briefcase. I carried it with me every day, often under my arm. When I studied, I put it on the library table, under my books, with only the name showing. Sometimes I even opened it and pretended to be reading it. At night I kept it in a safe place, away from light so it wouldn't fade.

My plan worked beautifully! My copy of the *Journal* looked current. I looked intelligent and aware.

For two years I carried that paper everywhere. Then it happened. Near the end of my last year in law school, while I was sitting in the student lounge killing time, a friend asked to borrow my copy of the *Journal*. Fortunately, I had anticipated such a disaster. My contingency plan was in place. I nodded, reached out, and knocked my cup of coffee over onto the paper. My friend moved on. My secret was safe.

It saddened me to throw away the soggy remains of my one and only copy of the *Journal*, but I had no choice.

I didn't buy another. Graduation was only six weeks away, and it didn't seem like a good investment under the circumstances. Besides, my reputation was already made.

The *Wall Street Journal*. An American institution. The daily diary of the American dream.

Is that really true? For that matter, what is the American dream? Do all Americans have the same dream? What does the *Journal* think that dream is?

From the looks of the *Journal*'s pages, one might believe the answer to be simple and straightforward. The American dream is success. It is accumulated wealth. It is power. It is high income, successful investments, and all the trappings that go with them.

Or is it?

Several weeks after seeing that commercial, I was sitting next to a friend on a flight from St. Louis to Nashville. He was reading. I was writing. As always, I didn't want to be disturbed.

"I know this guy," he said, breaking my train of thought. He handed me his copy of that day's *Journal* and pointed to a front-page article. He was obviously impressed. I was, too. If the *Journal* is the diary of the American dream, being featured on its pages must be the ultimate stamp of approval.

I began to read. The plane's engines droned on.

The article was about a man named William Bevins, one of those behind-the-scenes geniuses who supposedly makes the wheels of commerce go forward smoothly.

This Bevins fellow was described as the "front line

manager who fills in the complex financial details" for millionaire Ted Turner, enabling the fruits of Turner's imagination to be turned into reality. According to the article, the thirty-nine-year-old Bevins was definitely "not a 'yes man,' " but was characterized instead as "his own man," and one who performs "superbly." *Respected* and *sophisticated* were two of the words used. This "slight, bespectacled accountant from East Tennessee" was described as a "high-IQ individual" and "a brilliant CFO" by one of his fellow workers.

"Wow," I muttered softly. "Pretty impressive." I read on. There was more.

Such praise was not without its price. Because of Turner Broadcasting's small finance staff, Bevins was said to be "the most overworked person in the world" by another fellow executive. The "grueling schedule" he had been on for months, maybe even years, had taken its toll. He had suffered a heart attack in his office three years earlier, at the age of thirty-six. He "appears to be doing fine now," said a friend. He had quit smoking, but had started up again because of the pressure.

Being "on the go from early morning to late evening" had taken its toll on his family life. He had two marriages to his credit, and two divorces. Nonetheless he still "follows the sun" in search of pleasure, and gets to the Caribbean "as often as possible."

He was described as a nice guy with a dry sense of humor, but one whose humor wasn't always appreciated. One fellow worker had found it necessary to punch him out in a bar. "I belted him once," the fellow worker confirmed. "He deserved it. He said something stupid."

My God, I thought. Is this the American dream? Is this really newsworthy? Are we so caught up in the quest for wealth and power that someone can be congratulated for achieving something that cost him two broken marriages and a heart attack before he reached forty?

I handed the paper back to my traveling companion and

muttered something about being impressed. I wasn't, though. I didn't feel like writing anymore, so I closed my eyes and tried to get some sleep.

I forgot about that article until a few weeks later. I was reminded of it when I found myself in another place, heading for a visit with another behind-the-scenes genius, another mover-and-shaker who had searched for, and had supposedly found, the American dream.

There was no sign out front, yet I was certain this was the place. The desk clerk at the Marriott had been very specific. "You'll see a large dairy farm with a sign out front," he had said. "The next driveway to the right is the one you are looking for." I had just passed the dairy farm and here was the driveway. This had to be it, but the tiny guardhouse was empty and the gate was open.

I hadn't expected the gate to be open.

The brick gate and guardhouse looked as though they might signal the entrance to one of those new subdivisions where they charge a bundle for the houses and put up a fancy entrance to make you think the houses are worth it. I maneuvered my rental car between the gateposts and headed on up the long winding drive. The grassy fields on either side of the drive were freshly mowed, but sparsely landscaped and void of animals or people. The monotony was broken only by the long white fence that separated this property from the dairy farm next door. The driveway climbed a hill and curved to the left. As I topped the rise, I saw what I was looking for.

Straight ahead was a large building of classic design in red brick, with several rows of identical windows. It had a cupola on its roof and an impressive set of double doors front and center. It had an aura of solidarity. It looked as if it ought to be in Philadelphia or Boston, or some other historic place. It looked that way except for the bars on the windows, and the sign. Chiseled in stone above the double doors were the words LEXINGTON FEDERAL COR-RECTIONAL INSTITUTION.

I parked the car and walked up to the door.

I was actually surprised to find that this door was locked. I had been lulled into a false sense of casualness by the pastoral setting, the open gate, and the absence of fences. But reality finally returned. A uniformed guard stared back at me through a glass panel in the door.

The guard looked me up and down. I must have seemed harmless in my business suit and starched shirt. An instant later the latch clanked loudly and the door swung open. Another guard motioned for me to come to a desk, where he gave me a form to fill out.

Did I have any weapons? I checked "no." Any drugs? Another "no." Any electronic equipment? I made a note about my portable tape recorder and my hearing aids. Fortunately, they weren't on the forbidden list. Was I a member of any group that advocated the overthrow of the United States government by force or violence? Again I checked "no." I couldn't help wondering if anyone would be stupid enough to check "yes" on that one.

I turned in the form and was directed toward an electronic gate. Apparently I had passed muster again.

Once inside, I approached another man at another desk. "Who do you want to see?" he asked, unconcerned with such niceties as grammatical correctness. I answered his question. "He'll be right down," the man continued. "Sit over there." He directed me toward a row of spartan government-issue chairs.

The room was painted an institutional noncolor. There was a lot of activity, with people constantly scurrying in and out. Most of the people were dressed alike, in identical denim shirts and jeans, and plain shoes. There were no numbers, no stripes, and no chains on the ankles, but it was easy to tell what they were. The only thing I couldn't tell was which one was the one I was there to see. I had seen pictures, but they had been taken in his three-piece suit days, with a look of authority on his face and a gold Rolex on his wrist. I had no pictures of him in denim.

A slender, graying man came through the gate. He was, in a word, ordinary. He eyed me suspiciously, sat in a chair opposite mine, lit a cigarette, and stared at me.

I don't know what I had expected, but this wasn't it. He looked like the kind of fellow I might find myself sitting next to at a ball game, or standing in line behind at the hardware store on a Saturday morning. He didn't look like a monetary genius, or a power broker, or a financial wizard, or any of the other things he had been called in recent years. He didn't look like the kind of man who could make or break others on a whim. He didn't look like a man whose yes or no might well determine who would be rich and who wouldn't. He didn't look like a manipulator who would waste his years helping build a financial house of cards which, when it finally fell, would sweep himself and others into the restricting confines of this kind of place, leaving behind a trail of shame.

But then, what do those kinds of people look like? Prison denim is, after all, a great equalizer.

I gathered my courage, approached him, extended my hand, and introduced myself.

"I'm David Crabtree," he said. He looked at me with an expression that was an odd mixture of old arrogance and new embarrassment. He returned my handshake but remained seated. He glanced my way but didn't look me in the eye.

David Crabtree. Architect and engineer of a banking empire. Millionaire, resident of a mansion, owner of an airplane, controller of the cash flow, mover and shaker, decision maker. The kind of man who, at one time, may well have rated an article of his own in the *Wall Street Journal*.

Several hours later, when I was on a plane headed back to Nashville, I was able to relax and reflect on the events of that day. When I did, my mind couldn't help wandering back to that commercial, and to the daily diary of the American dream.

What do we dream about? What do we want? Is it wrong to seek wealth? Is power a bad thing in itself? Is financial security an unattainable illusion?

All of these questions rattled around in my tired brain, these and many others besides. I had lots of questions, but precious few answers.

Is there a middle ground? Are we all headed in the wrong direction? Not everyone on the fast track ends up divorced or in prison. I was on a pretty fast track myself, after all. Much of my energy had gone in a similar direction. Was that wrong, too?

By the time I got home that evening, I was genuinely troubled. I remembered the words of Jesus, when he told us to "seek ye first his kingdom and his righteousness, and all these things will be yours as well." I prayed about it. I asked God for an answer.

For me, the answer came several months later, and several hundred miles away, from an unlikely source. It came from a gentle, genial man named Will Terry, Dean of Students at Davidson College, and it came in his remarks to the incoming freshman class, which included my daughter Lindy. Barbara and I had come to deliver her to a brand new world, one that excited her and frightened us.

Dean Terry was a graying, fatherly type who appeared to have genuine concern for the children we were about to leave in his care. Leaving Lindy wouldn't be easy, but he seemed to be the right man to take over. He said all the things a father needed to hear in the moments before he was to leave his daughter in an alien world.

Most of his remarks were directed at the students. He talked about the unhappiness that haunted some young people during their first year away from home, an unhappiness that could grow to major proportions and lead to dropping out, or even to suicide. He talked about the "starting over" phenomenon, how some unhappy young people looked at college as their second chance and were disappointed to find that nothing has changed, and that they were still the same persons. He had a piece of advice for those in the audience who were coming to college in search of happiness, advice that struck me so profoundly that I scribbled it down on a piece of paper.

"If you have come here looking for happiness," he said, "you will be disappointed. Happiness is a by-product of life. It isn't something you strive for, it is something that results from a life well lived."

That's so true, I thought. It's true not just for happiness, but also for success, for self-satisfaction, and for all the good feelings of life, for all the things that make life worth living. These things are by-products of a good life, a life well lived, a life spent in daily communion with God. But if you make these things your goals, if success or self-satisfaction or happiness is what you strive for, you will inevitably fail.

All of a sudden David Crabtree came to mind. So did William Bevins. So did myself.

These words from the sixth chapter of Matthew also came to mind. "Seek first his kingdom and his righteousness, and all these things shall be yours as well." Jesus' meaning was clear at last. The "things" of this world are not goals for us to strive for. They are by-products of life. They come when they are not pursued.

Can we have our cake and eat it, too? Is this some kind of "deal" between us and Jesus, a deal that lets us in the back door even though the front door is locked? Does this mean that we can get everything we want, as long as we don't go chasing after it?

No. This isn't a deal. It's just a promise.

Trust in me and I'll take care of you. That's the essence of what Jesus was saying. I know what you worry about, and I know what you want. I also know what you *need*, and I know what it takes to be happy, content, and at peace. This is what I'll do for you. Trust me. Follow me.

Is the American dream really to be found on the pages of the *Wall Street Journal?* Judge for yourself. It may seem so sometimes. I can't answer that question for anyone but myself, but I can tell you this. My dream, and I suspect the secret dream of every human being who has ever walked the face of this earth, is the dream of true happiness, contentment, and peace. It's the dream of loving relationships and meaningful experiences. *That* dream is found on the pages of the Bible, in the words of Jesus Christ. It's a dream that can come true for every one of us.

MAKING MEMORIES

How old do boys have to be to join the Cub Scouts? Nine? Ten? Eleven? Are they third graders? Fourth graders? I just can't remember. I know that my son Richard was a Cub Scout a long time ago, and he's twenty-one now. I think he was nine when he joined. Maybe ten. Perhaps it will come to me.

I was a Cub Scout once. I don't remember how old I was, either. I remember going to the meetings, and I remember Mrs. Carpenter, our den mother. She's in her nineties now, and is as patient and gentle as she was back then. Other than that, I recall very little about the experience, except for the uniform. And the "official" Cub Scout knife. And the canteen. And the binoculars. And all of that other wonderful stuff. But most of all the uniform.

It was back in the late forties or early fifties. My family had just moved to Nashville. I had never even heard of Cub Scouts before then, but in Nashville scouting was the thing to do. All my friends looked forward to joining up. When the time came, I joined, too. I didn't know what to expect from the experience, but I wanted to be wherever my friends were, doing whatever they were doing. Besides, as I said before, I really liked the uniform.

I can still remember the first time I ever saw a Cub Scout uniform.

Back then there was only one shopping center in Nashville. It was called "downtown." It was a lot like a mall, I suppose, except that the stores were more spread out and there was no roof over the open space. There were also no ferns, no T-shirt shops, no benches, and no food courts, and cars could drive right up to the stores. It was clean and safe and easily accessible by bus. I could go there alone, without fear for what might happen to me. It was great fun.

I have fond memories of riding the Woodmont shuttle bus over to West End Avenue, transferring to the West End Local at the old green shed, getting off at Fourth and Church, scurrying over to Harvey's Bakery to buy a cream-filled horn or something equally messy and delicious, then sitting in the very front row at the Knickerbocker Theater and watching whatever adventure Randolph Scott was up to next. My mother could always tell where I had been, because most of the powdered sugar from that delicious horn ended up on my lap.

But I digress. This isn't about the Knickerbocker Theater or cream horns or Randolph Scott. It's about Cub Scouts. I mentioned downtown only because I was talking about Cub Scout uniforms, and that's where Burks was.

Burks was a large old store with tall columns holding up its high ceilings, dark wooden floors that creaked, and elaborate elevators with ornate gates that clanked when they were opened and shut by *live* elevator operators. It was a quiet place with dignified salespeople who appeared to be as old and conservative as the store itself, and who always glared at me as I scurried across the main floor, headed for the elevators. I always headed straight for the elevators. There was nothing on the first floor to interest me. Nothing on the second floor, either. But the third floor was heaven.

The third floor housed the boys' department. But that wasn't all. It also housed the most wonderful hobby shop imaginable, filled with toy soldiers, model airplane kits, electric trains, miniature villages, stacks of balsa wood, racks of model airplane dope, and all sorts of tools and supplies. I could browse for hours. And, as if that weren't enough, tucked into a small corner of the third floor was the scouting shop.

My first trip to the scouting shop took my breath away! They had everything! Uniforms! Pocketknives! Canteens! Binoculars! Everything a boy could dream of and more, all resplendent in dark blue and bright gold, trimmed in polished brass, proudly bearing the official Cub Scout emblem for all the world to see. Forget about the dull green stuff the older Scouts had to wear. Give me the blue and gold! It was gorgeous!

I don't know what others might have thought, but as far as I am concerned, I never looked better in my whole life than I did the day I first put on my dark blue Cub Scout uniform, slid the brass tip of my dark blue woven belt through its bright brass buckle, adjusted my gold scarf by sliding up the official brass whatchamacallit, slipped my official Cub Scout pocketknife into my pocket, and headed for my first meeting.

Frankly, I wasn't a very good Scout. In spite of the uniform, in spite of the official Cub Scout pocketknife, in spite of the canteen and the binoculars and whatever else my parents bought me, in spite of my father spending two years as a Scout leader, it just never "took" with me. It was true back then and it's still true today. I was made for the front row of the Knickerbocker Theater, not for the great outdoors. I wanted to *own* the knife, not *use* it.

So, many years later, when son Richard was a Cub Scout and I finally experienced my first camping adventure, the mere fact that I had *lived* through it was motivation enough to send me to the typewriter. What follows is the essay I wrote after that adventure. It was first published in *Scouting* magazine, and it marked the first time I was ever paid for writing something.

The note came home from school, stuffed into Richard's lunch box, surrounded by the usual collection of grossly unappetizing remnants. Notes from school usually didn't carry good news. They invariably meant one of two things. Either it was time for another conference with the teacher, or the school was trying to raise money again. But this one was different. It was from the Cub Scout troop leader and was addressed to all Cub Scout parents:

CUB SCOUT CAMPOUT
APRIL 20-22
MARK YOUR CALENDARS NOW!
EACH BOY *MUST* BE ACCOMPANIED BY
HIS FATHER OR ANOTHER ADULT

"Can we go, Dad? Can we go?"

I looked down at Richard's sparkling eyes. They were filled with anticipation. I thought about all the other times he had come to me. "Are you working tonight, Dad?" he would ask, his voice filled with anticipation. "Are you busy?" Far too often I offered some lame excuse instead of pitching ball or shooting baskets or just sitting and talking. I made myself a little promise. *This* time it would be different.

"You *bet* we'll go! We wouldn't miss it for the world."

"Oh boy!" he shouted, throwing his arms around my neck, almost knocking me off balance. Then he ran off to tell his two older sisters, while I put my glasses back on straight. "We're going camping!" he yelled out as he ran through the house. "We're going camping!"

Fear gripped me. I eased back into my chair and began to think about what I had gotten myself into.

Frankly, the whole idea made me nervous. I was definitely not cut out to be a woodsman. I had learned that years ago, and there was no reason to ever expect anything different.

When I was nine or ten, my parents bought me a war surplus jungle hammock and an air mattress. The jungle hammock was neat! It had tent flaps that spread out and hovered above it like giant wings, and mosquito netting that could be zipped closed from the inside. It was great looking. I was thrilled to death!

On the very first night, full of excitement, I carried my hammock out into the backyard and set up camp. Our tiny lot didn't have such luxuries as trees, only the little sticks my dad and I had planted, sticks that hadn't had time to grow much by the time I reached jungle-hammock age. So I tied one rope to a fence post not fifty feet from our back door, then tied the other to a swing frame. I almost made myself sick blowing up the air mattress and had a devil of a time getting it inside the hammock, not realizing that I was supposed to put it in first and *then* blow it up. Finally, though, I settled in for the evening.

Things went along fine until the sun went down, about the time I zipped up the mosquito netting and settled in for the night. *That's* when the noises started. I don't know if it was a goblins convention or what. Whatever the reason, every ghost and spirit in our end of town picked that evening to play in our yard. The night was filled with strange noises, each of which conjured images of untold horror in my mind. I was convinced that disaster lay just outside the confines of my net-covered hideaway. I squeezed my eyes shut, deathly afraid to look around, afraid my house wouldn't be there.

I endured as much fear as I could possibly stand, then called it quits. At approximately eight-thirty, I untied the jungle hammock, deflated the air mattress, rolled them up neatly, and marched back indoors, determined to stay forever. I had succeeded, too, until that note arrived.

I stared at the crumpled paper. It was inconceivable to me that I would be able to shed my old prejudices and change my ways in time for the campout. But how could I possibly let young Richard down?

For weeks I anticipated the big event. Richard did, too. He talked about nothing else except the need to sharpen our knives, check our flashlight batteries, and finish the "buddy burners" which we were supposed to use to cook our meals. In spite of his enthusiasm, my anticipation began to feel suspiciously like dread. The troop leader was obviously unaware of my distress. When the list of needed supplies came home a week or so in advance of the big date, Valium was conspicuously absent.

A few days before our scheduled departure, I began to panic. I summoned my courage and called a friend who knew me well. He was incredulous, but agreed to lend me two sleeping bags. "You're not really going through with this, are you?" he asked. I assured him that I was determined to succeed, no matter what. "Well, just don't get any dew in your ear," he quipped. Big help!

Time marched on. At the last possible moment I faced reality and put together the remaining necessities.

My apprehension peaked the night before our departure when the weather took a turn for the worse. A cold rain moved in from the west. The forecast for the weekend was bleak. I could just see myself catching pneumonia. I would be a living sacrifice on the altar of fatherhood.

Finally the big day came. We gathered at Camp Boxwell, on the shores of Old Hickory Lake near Nashville. There we were, fifteen Cubs, one gung ho leader, and a motley group of fathers who wondered collectively, albeit silently, what in the world we were doing there. I still wonder if any of them felt as out of place as I did. By actual measurement we were less than two miles from the nearest all-night market, but it seemed like a wilderness to me.

We spent most of the first afternoon figuring out how to set up our borrowed tents. Once that was done, we started a fire. Before long, we had gathered around it for our first meal together. One of the young Cubs was called on to return thanks. He took off his cap and shuffled nervously while the leader struggled to get the others to be quiet at the same time, a virtually impossible task. Finally some semblance of order was accomplished. We bowed our heads and listened as the lad spoke from his heart.

"Dear God," he said in a barely audible voice, "bless this food, and help us live through this camp."

Amen, I thought.

That prayer broke the tension for all of us, and we did, in fact, manage to live through the camp in spite of the unseasonal cold. The three days passed in a heartbeat.

I taught young Richard everything I knew during the first twenty minutes or so, and we spent the rest of the time learning together. We went hiking and fishing, cooked our own meals (Glory be, the buddy burners worked!), learned to use several different tools, and even revived the almost lost art of mumblety-peg.

I shared Richard's fascination and his glee as he wolfed down the over-done egg he had fried on the burner he had made. I watched him build a fire from scratch. We shared these and a thousand other happy experiences. In the process I learned some of the basic maxims of camping, such as not to let fifteen Cub Scouts cook my dinner if I had a problem eating dirt, and not to stick my bare feet into a nylon sleeping bag on a thirty-five degree night.

I was amazed at how much I could enjoy food cooked over an open fire after a day in the woods, when I never would have *touched* the same food at home. I was astounded at how much there is to see in the woods when there's a small boy at my side willing to point everything out to me. And there is nothing better than fresh brewed coffee at daybreak, when the dew (which never made it to my ear, incidentally) hangs heavy over the stillness of the forest floor.

All too soon, Sunday came. Time to break camp. We enjoyed our last meal together out under the open sky, then set about dismantling the tents.

In short order, everything was neatly folded and packed

away. The boys spent their last few minutes running around the area, using up some of their limitless energy. I wandered back to the spot in the woods where our tent had been. There was a clearly defined square in the grass where the sun's rays had been blocked by my "home" of the past three days. A cool breeze wandered through, on its way to somewhere else. It was quiet, except for the chatter of the boys off in the distance.

Standing in the middle of that square, I felt a deep sense of peace and satisfaction, and I heard the gentle whisper of God's voice, just as Elijah heard it thousands of years ago on the mountain at Horeb.

I uttered a prayer of my own.

"Thank you, God," I said softly. "This will make a really nice memory."

That's what had been going on, you know. Memory making. Storing up treasures to use later on. Sure, we had learned a lot about camping and cooking and using tools, but if we never use those skills again, that's okay. We had spent our time wisely, creating memories that will last both of us for a lifetime.

What could be more important than memory making? What could be more valuable for a man, or a woman, than a storehouse of pleasant memories? They are our private catalog of special times, ready for recall at a moment's notice.

Someday, if I am very fortunate, Richard and I will be sitting around talking with his son, and this particular memory will suddenly return. One of us will say, "Remember the time we went camping together?" The other will say, "Yes, I remember!" Then we'll laugh together and share once again the good time we had at old Camp Boxwell, eating dirt and making memories.

——

Well, that's the old essay. I hadn't thought about it until recently, when I saw an article in our local paper.

The article was an announcement that a young man

from Nashville had been named the top collegiate debater in the United States at the National Debate Tournament in San Antonio, Texas. The young man who had accomplished this singular triumph was someone I knew, although I hadn't seen him in years. His name was T. A. McKinney, and he was one of the fifteen Cub Scouts on our camping trip.

I probably couldn't name more than three or four of the boys who made up that group. It happened too long ago. Some of them remained friends of young Richard, but most of them didn't. Most went their separate ways. Yet I still remember T. A., and I remember his father. I didn't know his father all that well, and I no longer remember his name. I remember his courage, though. I remember his courage.

The note had made it very clear. The boys couldn't come unless their fathers came with them. T. A. McKinney wanted to come, so his father had come too, even though it would be an ordeal. You see, he was very ill at the time. More than just ill, really. He was dying, and we all knew it.

Mr. McKinney couldn't participate in many of the planned activities, but he did what he could. I especially remember him and T. A. sitting on the bank next to the lake, holding fishing poles and enjoying the quiet together. There was a melancholy sadness about that scene, but there was a lot of strength there, too.

You could tell the man was hurting, but he never complained and never asked for help. He just kept going. He couldn't sleep outside in a tent exposed to the elements, so he slept alone in the back of a station wagon, parked near the campsite. He was determined to be there. He was determined that his son wouldn't have to miss that experience. He stayed the whole time, too. I'll never forget it.

A few weeks later he was dead.

I cannot tell you that there is any direct connection

between the father's presence at that camping trip and the son's work ethic and success, but I can tell you this: whenever we participate in a significant way in the lives of our children, or in the lives of *any* of the people we really care about, we are doing more than having a good time and making memories. We are making an investment that will pay off handsomely for them and for us.

Of all the treasures God has entrusted to us, the most precious of all is the treasure of other human beings. Whether it's our children, our spouses, our families, or our friends, *these* are the pearls of great price. Our fond memories are only part of the dividends we earn when we invest our time and turn our attention to the people in our lives. The real return on our investment goes far beyond what we can know and understand.

The nicest thing I can think of would be to appear before God's throne at the end of our lives with hearts full of warm memories to share with our Creator, much like the wise men spread their gifts before the Christ child. God would like that, too, wouldn't he?

No, I don't know if there is a connection or not. But I've got a hunch that any man who would do what T. A.'s father did that weekend had probably been making that kind of wise investment for years. I've got another hunch, too, or maybe it's just a hope. I hope that wherever he is, T. A.'s father knows about his son's outstanding achievement. If he does, I'll bet he's very, very proud.

THE BLESSED ASSURANCE
OF CHRISTMAS

It was just after 11:30 in the evening, Greenwich mean time, and I wasn't in a very good mood.

Why do they call it "mean" time anyway? At that precise moment, of course, mean was the right word for it. I was harboring a mean spirit. We were late, and as always, I didn't think it was my fault. I was angry at the rest of my family for failing to follow my example of promptness.

The driver did his best to get us there on time. The shiny black taxi sped along the broad boulevard that snaked its way alongside the Thames River. I stared out across the murky water at the incongruous reflection of tawdry modern skyscrapers on the other side. This was London. Those ugly buildings didn't look like they belonged there. It was Christmas Eve. My feelings of anger and resentment didn't belong there, either.

I turned my attention to our side of the river. The intricate facades of the buildings of old London made me grateful once again for the preservation of the past.

As usual, I was riding backwards. That didn't help my mood any. Barby, Lindy, and Barbara occupied the spacious bench seat, while young Richard and I scrunched ourselves into the minuscule jumpseats that would slap shut as soon as we got out. No wonder the girls liked to ride in cabs. Who wouldn't enjoy leaning back in plush comfort, watching world-class scenery race by? Precious little could be seen from my jumpseat unless I turned my head sideways, and when I did that, my head bumped against the roof. It had been that way all week. By the time we got anywhere, I was usually battered and bruised and too stiff to move. The cramped quarters fueled my distress as the few remaining seconds ticked on by.

In this instance, a cab had been the only choice. There was no direct tube from Westminster to St. Paul's, and had there been one, we couldn't have afforded the time it would take to find a station and wait for a train. Only minutes earlier I had learned that my long-planned Christmas Eve adventure, the *one thing* I wanted to be sure to do while I was in England, wasn't going to happen. Westminster was a sellout. Not even standing room. So off we went, scooting along Victoria Embankment in our own personal sardine can, headed for the commoners' cathedral, St. Paul's.

Anger and disappointment were my companions. Fortunately, they didn't hang around once we got there.

How can I describe it? Goosebumps times four.

It started in the cab when Lindy peered out of the window and exclaimed, "What's that?" I did my best to twist my body around so I could see where she was pointing. It was painful, but worth it. Hovering over the rows of buildings like a giant rising sun was a huge granite dome, bathed in orange light, dwarfing the surrounding rooftops. Christopher Wren's masterpiece loomed ahead, patiently awaiting the arrival of our tardy group of foreigners.

"That's St. Paul's," I said. "That's where we're going." I suddenly felt better about the change of plans.

Minutes later we were scurrying up the stairs Charles and Di had first walked down as husband and wife.

Better make that goosebumps times ten.

St. Paul's goes on forever! I'd never seen anything so vast, so seemingly endless. And the hugeness of it was emphasized by its incredible beauty. The shining mosaics that line the vaulting archways are indescribable, as are the sparkling, multicolored windows and the intricate wood and gold carvings. It is as if God had wanted to share his jewel box with us, and had simply turned it upside down on that very spot, letting all of its splendor hang from its ceiling and cascade down its sides.

At the far, far end was a huge, glittering mosaic of Jesus Christ, his outstretched arms beckoning us to come, his pleading eyes urging us to believe.

We moved along with the crowd. The seats were all gone. We finally found a place where we could stand. That was all right. At least we were there.

The music began. Three thousand voices sang out as one: "Joy to the world, the Saviour reigns, let men their songs employ." Booming bass notes rumbled from the massive organ, making the very rafters ring. The words rose slowly from the surface of the church and began to fill the chamber. When the sound reached the top it slapped against the vaulted arches, exploding into pieces and raining down over the still-singing worshipers. At the end of each verse the organist had to stop and wait for several seconds while the remaining sound floated down and faded away.

If you ever want to describe a fireworks display to one who cannot see, take him to St. Paul's and let him listen to the singing. That's what it's like. Shimmering pieces of sound drift downward like millions of sparks scattered by exploding rockets.

Soon it was time for Communion. An endless line of humanity shuffled its way toward the altar. I glanced at my watch. It was almost twelve. I suddenly realized that we were only a few short miles from Greenwich, the place where time begins. God was about to deliver Christmas to St. Paul's, to be properly consecrated and passed on to the rest of the world.

"This is his body, broken for you," the priest said. "This

is his blood, shed for you." Soon it was midnight. The second hand had climbed past twelve and had started its descent. Christmas had begun its westward journey. It had rolled into St. Paul's like a mighty tide, engulfing all of us who had come to that beautiful place at that special time. I thanked God for letting me be there, then kissed Christmas good-bye with my heart, sending it on its way.

I am grateful for that moment. I truly understood, perhaps for the very first time, that we really are one in the spirit, one in the word. All over the world, Christians were moving toward their houses of worship, preparing to do what we had just done, those of us lucky enough to be in the place where Christmas begins.

That year, the indescribable St. Paul's dominated my Christmas memories. The next year, however, it was Decatur Church of Christ in Decatur, Georgia, a church that is a great deal smaller than St. Paul's and a lot easier to describe.

The Decatur Church of Christ is situated on Old Highway 78, beyond downtown Decatur, two miles inside the huge perimeter highway that encircles Atlanta. Finding it would have been impossible had it not been for the ad in the yellow pages.

The service was scheduled to start at ten, and it was exactly ten when I arrived. My plane had left Nashville on time that morning, but had hovered over Atlanta for what seemed like an eternity, waiting for the fog to lift. I remember the pilot saying something about landing in Macon, seventy-five miles away, but fortunately that didn't happen. Nonetheless it was nine-thirty by the time I got my rental car, and Decatur is a long way from the airport. Thanks to the ad, I knew exactly where to go.

From the highway, Decatur Church of Christ looks like one of those churches that will probably add a sanctuary some day. It's situated on a tiny lot, and when the crowd is big, latecomers have to park in a shopping center lot nearby. On this December morning the crowd was huge. A man directed me into the church's front drive. I felt welcome. Another man directed me to drive on out the back way. I was totally confused. I finally figured it out, though. I followed the other cars to the shopping center and was soon walking back to the church.

Appearances are deceiving. There really is a sanctuary in that church, one which seats perhaps four hundred people. It's downhill from the main building as one approaches the church and is more or less hidden from view. But it is definitely there, and on this cold December morning it was packed.

All the seats were taken when I arrived. The ushers were opening folding chairs as fast as they could. I sat on one and waited. Within minutes the portable chair supply had been exhausted. People began standing along the walls. Once the walls were filled, the rest just waited in the lobby, unable to see a thing, but content to be there.

It was remarkably quiet. I stared at the unadorned expanse of textured brick that formed the backdrop for the church's pulpit. Behind the pulpit were three empty chairs, surrounded by an array of flowers that took my breath away.

Twenty-four hours earlier I had been finishing a leisurely breakfast at home, sipping coffee, glancing at the morning paper. A story had caught my eye. Three young men with ties to Nashville had been found dead in a car in a remote area near Decatur. According to the article, one of the young men was the grandson of a prominent Nashvillian. I didn't know the family. How sad, I had thought as I turned the page.

A few hours later, Barbara had called my office.

"I have some awful news," she had said. "Two of those boys were Charlie's sons!"

Her words had slammed into my gut, slicing my heart in two as they passed by. The heartache was still there as I settled into my folding chair at the back of the church.

Charlie was one of my best friends in high school. He

was a jewel. He still is. So is Kay, his wife. I love them both. We had lost contact for a while, as friends often do, but in recent years we had seen them often. The boys, Don, Tim, and Patrick, had been in our home. Charlie is a writer, and just lately our common interest in writing had put a new spark in our old friendship.

The thing I remember most about Charlie as a teenager is that he was a Christian. Lots of us were Christians on Sunday, but Charlie was one all the time. He lived his faith without embarrassment or hesitation. God's love permeated every aspect of his life, making everything he did a witness. There was nothing oppressive about it. He was just a constant, unwavering example. He wouldn't compromise, and if you were lucky enough to be his friend, you knew what it was to be loved without demands and without conditions.

That's what made the whole unbelievable experience so damningly difficult. If God were to have come to earth that day and were to have asked me who, among men, was worthy of his kingdom, I would have said, "Lord, take a look at Charlie Walton." Yet here I was, part of an overflow crowd at Decatur Church of Christ on a Wednesday morning in December, swallowing sobs and watching through tear-blurred eyes as three identical caskets rolled down the aisle, two of them carrying the earthly remains of Charlie's sons. It just didn't make any sense. Maddening frustration welled within and spilled out.

I still remember the feelings that swirled around in my heart and the thoughts that filled my mind.

Is this fair? Is this right? Does all this stuff I believe really have any meaning? Why bother believing in *anything*? It rains and storms on the just and the unjust, while the God we worship seems powerless, or at best unwilling, to do anything about it.

Three fine young men. Boys, really. Sure, there was an explanation; they were yielding to temptation, as humans often do. But they were boys! Good boys, not bad ones.

Boys whose hearts burned with enthusiasm, boys whose eyes sparkled with the innate goodness that God had put there just before kissing them good-bye and sending them off to their earthly homes. And now, God was taking them back. Three lives had been snuffed out. Three caskets were rolling down the aisle, headed for a common grave. Two families were leaning on each other for support. And on the sidelines was the Devil himself, gloating fiendishly, marking up another victory.

I felt absolutely no love for God as I sat there. I felt only anger, dismay, and disbelief. Prayer was the farthest thing from my mind. Pray? To a God who'd allow the likes of this to happen? No thank you.

The preacher rose to speak.

Right from the start he admitted to harboring the same feelings that were haunting me. It was comforting to know that my thoughts were shared, that I wasn't alone. "I don't know what to say," he admitted. "I have no explanation for why these things happen." Neither did I.

The preacher said something personal about each of the boys, meaningful things about the fun they'd had together, the dreams, hopes, and aspirations they'd shared. He acknowledged the families' losses and the feelings that no doubt had to be present in their hearts. Feelings like anger, despair, and disbelief. He was right on target. Those very feelings were being shared by all of us who had gathered there.

He read the familiar words of comfort from I Corinthians. "O death, where is thy victory? O death, where is thy sting? . . . Thanks be to God who gives us the victory through our Lord Jesus Christ." Then he reminded us of how much love and support those two families were going to need. As I sat and listened, I was aware of how glad I was that I had come. It was the right thing to do. Most of the time, being there is the only thing you *can* do.

Finally the preacher sat down. Then the song leader rose. "The family has selected some songs," he said.

"You've got to be kidding," I muttered while everyone else reached for a songbook. "Sing? At a time like this?" But sing they did, and with an enthusiasm that I had never witnessed before and may never see again. The three thousand voices at St. Paul's paled into insignificance as five hundred hearts declared their faith in song.

It was at that precise moment that the truth finally filtered through my anger and settled into my hardened heart. If the Devil had any thought of triumph in his grisly heart over the death of those three young men, that thought was buried forever in a wave of music, born in the depths of despair but carried forth on the wings of faith.

> When peace, like a river, attendeth my way,
> when sorrows like sea billows roll;
> whatever my lot, thou hast taught me to say,
> It is well, it is well with my soul.

The sound exploded gloriously into God's world like a beautiful red sunrise on a cold, crisp day. It came alive inside my heart like an old friend almost forgotten, but suddenly recognized. I opened my hymnal and joined in. In spite of myself, I sang. It was impossible *not* to sing.

You see, a miracle was occurring that day at Decatur Church of Christ, and I wanted to be a part of it. Five hundred people were witnessing to the reality of God's victory over death. Five hundred people understood the importance of God's gift to us, and what it meant to each of them in times when nothing else would help. There wasn't a dry eye in the place, and there wasn't a single person who had escaped the truth. Victory is ours, no matter what. The Devil hadn't won that day—not at all!

> Though Satan should buffet, though trials should come,
> let this blest assurance control,
> that Christ has regarded my helpless estate,
> and hath shed his own blood for my soul.

These words capture the very essence of Christmas. Christ was born so that he might die. Christ was crucified so that we might live abundantly, without fear. It is, indeed, the Blessed Assurance, our help in ages past and our hope for years to come.

The enemy still lives, of course, and the struggle continues. The faithful still gather at Christmas, all over the world, to pay homage to the memory of a baby who grew to be a man like no other. And all over the world, the Blessed Assurance remains. It is true in the glory of St. Paul's, it is true in the simple beauty of Decatur Church of Christ, and it is true in a million other places. Ours is the victory if Jesus Christ is alive in our hearts. Ours is the victory if we are steadfast, immovable, and always abounding in the work of the Lord.

> My sin, oh, the bliss of this glorious thought!
> My sin, not in part but the whole,
> is nailed to the cross, and I bear it no more,
> praise the Lord, praise the Lord, O my soul!